STEAM TABLES

With Mollier Diagram
IN S.I. UN

R.S. KHURMI

S. CHAND & COMPANY LTD.

(AN ISO 9001: 2000 COMPANY)

RAM NAGAR, NEW DELHI-110 055

$$\eta = \dfrac{P}{Q_{in}} = \dfrac{P}{\frac{FC \cdot Cal.Val}{3600}} = \dfrac{3600}{Cal.Val} \cdot \dfrac{P}{FC} = \dfrac{3600}{Cal.Val} \cdot \dfrac{1}{SSC} \qquad SSC = \dfrac{FC}{P} \qquad CR = \dfrac{CV + SV}{CV}$$

$t_{in}^{-2\pi n}$

$P = m_{ef} \cdot S \cdot u \cdot n$

S. CHAND & COMPANY LTD.

(An ISO 9001 : 2000 Company)

Head Office: 7361, RAM NAGAR, NEW DELHI - 110 055
Phone: 23672080-81-82, 9899107446, 9911310888
Fax: 91-11-23677446
Shop at: schandgroup.com; e-mail: info@schandgroup.com

Branches:

AHMEDABAD	: 1st Floor, Heritage, Near Gujarat Vidhyapeeth, Ashram Road, **Ahmedabad** - 380 014, Ph: 27541965, 27542369, ahmedabad@schandgroup.com
BANGALORE	: No. 6, Ahuja Chambers, 1st Cross, Kumara Krupa-Road, **Bangalore** - 560 001, Ph: 22268048, 22354008, bangalore@schandgroup.com
BHOPAL	: 238-A, M.P. Nagar, Zone 1, **Bhopal** - 462 011, Ph: 4274723. bhopal@schandgroup.com
CHANDIGARH	: S.C.O. 2419-20, First Floor, Sector - 22-C (Near Aroma Hotel), **Chandigarh** -160 022, Ph: 2725443, 2725446, chandigarh@schandgroup.com
CHENNAI	: 152, Anna Salai, **Chennai** - 600 002, Ph: 28460026, chennai@schandgroup.com
COIMBATORE	: Plot No. 5, Rajalakshmi Nagar, Peelamedu, **Coimbatore** -641 004, (M) 09444228242, coimbatore@schandgroup.com
CUTTACK	: 1st Floor, Bhartia Tower, Badambadi, **Cuttack** - 753 009, Ph: 2332580; 2332581, cuttack@schandgroup.com
DEHRADUN	: 1st Floor, 20, New Road, Near Dwarká Store, **Dehradun** - 248 001, Ph: 2740889, 2740861, dehradun@schandgroup.com
GUWAHATI	: Pan Bazar, **Guwahati** - 781 001, Ph: 2738811, guwahati@schandgroup.com
HYDERABAD	: Sultan Bazar, **Hyderabad** - 500 195, Ph: 24651135, 24744815, hyderabad@schandgroup.com
JAIPUR	: A-14, Janta Store Shopping Complex, University Marg, Bapu Nagar, **Jaipur** - 302 015, Ph: 2719126, jaipur@schandgroup.com
JALANDHAR	: Mai Hiran Gate, **Jalandhar** - 144 008, Ph: 2401630, 5000630, jalandhar@schandgroup.com
JAMMU	: 67/B, B-Block, Gandhi Nagar, **Jammu** - 180 004, (M) 09878651464
KOCHI	: Kachapilly Square, Mullassery Canal Road, Ernakulam, **Kochi** - 682 011, Ph: 2378207, cochin@schandgroup.com
KOLKATA	: 285/J, Bipin Bihari Ganguli Street, **Kolkata** - 700 012, Ph: 22367459, 22373914, kolkata@schandgroup.com
LUCKNOW	: Mahabeer Market, 25 Gwynne Road, Aminabad, **Lucknow** - 226 018, Ph: 2626801, 2284815, lucknow@schandgroup.com
MUMBAI	: Blackie House, 103/5, Walchand Hirachand Marg, Opp. G.P.O., **Mumbai** - 400 001, Ph: 22690881, 22610885, mumbai@schandgroup.com
NAGPUR	: Karnal Bag, Model Mill Chowk, Umrer Road, **Nagpur** - 440 032, Ph: 2723901, 2777666 nagpur@schandgroup.com
PATNA	: 104, Citicentre Ashok, Govind Mitra Road, **Patna** - 800 004, Ph: 2300489, 2302100, patna@schandgroup.com
PUNE	: 291/1, Ganesh Gayatri Complex, 1st Floor, Somwarpeth, Near Jain Mandir, **Pune** - 411 011, Ph: 64017298, pune@schandgroup.com
RAIPUR	: Kailash Residency, Plot No. 4B, Bottle House Road, Shankar Nagar, **Raipur** - 492 007, Ph: 09981200834, raipur@schandgroup.com
RANCHI	: Flat No. 104, Sri Draupadi Smriti Apartments, East of Jaipal Singh Stadium, Neel Ratan Street, Upper Bazar, **Ranchi** - 834 001, Ph: 2208761, ranchi@schandgroup.com
VISAKHAPATNAM	: Plot No. 7, 1st Floor, Allipuram Extension, Opp. Radhakrishna Towers, Seethammadhara North Extn., **Visakhapatnam** - 530 013, (M) 09347580841, visakhapatnam@schandgroup.com

First Edition 1984
Subsequent Editions and Reprints 1984, 86, 87, 88, 89, 90, 91, 92, 93, 94, 96 (Twice), 97, 98 99, 2000, 2001, 2002, 2003, 2004 (Twice), 2005, 2006 (Twice), 2007 (Twice), 2008 (Twice)
Reprint 2009 (Twice)

ISBN : 81-219-0654-7   **Code : 10 044**

PRINTED IN INDIA

*By Rajendra Ravindra Printers Pvt. Ltd., 7361, Ram Nagar, New Delhi -110 055
and published by S. Chand & Company Ltd., 7361, Ram Nagar, New Delhi -110 055.*

(Handwritten marginal notes, right side:)

$$Q - U = \Delta U$$
$$\Delta U = m \int C_v d$$
$$pV = mRT$$
$$W = \int p\, dV$$
$$C_p = C_v + R$$
$$\frac{P_2}{P_1} = \left(\frac{V_1}{V_2}\right)$$
$$\frac{T_1}{T_2} = \left(\frac{P_1}{P_2}\right)$$
$$\frac{P_1}{P_2} = \left(\frac{}{}\right)$$
$$\frac{V_2}{V_1} = \left(\right.$$

(Handwritten note, bottom:)

$$\dot{Q} + \dot{m_1}\left(h_1 + \frac{c_1^2}{2} + z_1\right) = \frac{dE_s}{dt} + \dot{m_2}\left(h_2 + \frac{c_2^2}{2} + z_2\right) + \dot{W}$$

$\eta = \dfrac{\text{brake power}}{\text{indicated power}}$ $\dfrac{bmep}{imep}$ $\eta_{vol} = \dfrac{AC}{SV \cdot p \cdot n}$ $\text{Ideal air } SV \times \dfrac{n}{2} \times 60 \times p$.

$bsfc = \dfrac{FC}{power}$ $bmep = \dfrac{power}{SV \times \frac{n}{2}}$ $\eta_{vol}\ \dfrac{\text{actual air}}{\text{ideal air}}$ $AFR = \dfrac{\text{air cons}}{\text{fuel cons}}$

PREFACE TO THE EIGHTH EDITION

I feel happy in presenting the revised edition of this small booklet. The favourable and warm reception, which the previous editions and reprints of this booklet have enjoyed at home and abroad, has been a matter of great satisfaction to me. The mistakes, which had crept in the previous edition, have been eliminated. In short, it is earnestly hoped that this standard booklet will continue to earn appreciation of the teachers and students alike.

Although every care has been taken to check mistakes and misprints, in this colossal figure work, yet it is difficult to claim perfection. Any errors, omissions and suggestions for the improvement of this booklet brought to my notice, will be thankfully acknowledged and incorporated in the next edition.

R.S. KHURMI

PREFACE TO THE FIRST EDITION

I take an opportunity to present this small booklet entitled as *"Steam Tables in S.I. Units"* to the students of Degree, Diploma and A.M.I.E. (I) classes. The object of this booklet is to present the various properties of water and steam in a most concise, compact, to the point and lucid manner.

Although every care has been taken to check mistakes and misprints in the colossal figure work, yet it is difficult to claim perfection. Any errors, omissions and suggestions for the improvement of this booklet, brought to my notice, will be thankfully acknowledged and incorporated in the next edition.

R.S. KHURMI

λ $\gamma = \dfrac{C_p}{C_v}$

$C_p = \dfrac{\Sigma m C_p}{\Sigma m}$

RULES FOR S.I. UNITS

The International System of Units, abbreviated as S.I. Units, is a unified and systematically constituted system of fundamental and derived units for international use. This system of units is now being used in many countries, and it is hoped that it will be used throughout the world very soon. In India, the Standard of Weights and Measures Act of 1956 (wide which we switched over to M.K.S. Units) has been revised to recognised all the S.I. Units in Science and Technology as well as Industry and Commerce.

Though there are many rules for the style and usage of S.I. Units, yet the following are important from the subject point of view:

1. For a number, having 5 or more digits, the digits should be placed in groups of three, separated by space counting both to the left and right of the decimal point.

2. In a four digit number, the space is not required, unless the four digit number is used in a column of numbers with 5 or more digits.

Introduction to
Steam Tables and Mollier Diagram

1. Definition

Steam is the vapour form of water and is invisible when pure and dry. It does not obey the laws of perfect gases, until it is perfectly dry. When the dry steam is further heated, it behaves more or less like a perfect gas. The steam is, generally, used as a working substance in the operation of steam engines and steam turbines.

2. Formation of steam

The formation of steam takes place, when we continuously heat the water from any temperature in the following stages:

1. The volume of water slightly increases with the increase in temperature. But this increase is, generally, neglected for all types of calculations.

2. On further heating, the temperature of water reaches the boiling point. The boiling temperature of pure steam at normal atmospheric pressure of 1.013 bar (1.013×10^5 N/m^2 or 1.013×10^2 kN/m^2 also known as 1.013×10^5 kPa) is 100°C (373 K). But it increases with the increase in pressure.

3. After boiling point, the temperature remains constant. But the water starts evaporating and the volume of steam starts increasing. At this stage, the steam has some water particles in suspension and it is called wet steam. This process continues, till the whole water is converted into wet steam.

4. On further heating, the temperature of wet steam remains constant and all the water particles in suspension are converted into steam. At this stage, the steam is called dry saturated steam.

5. On further heating, the temperature of dry saturated steam starts increasing and it obeys the laws of perfect gases. At this stage, the steam is called superheated steam. As a matter fact, the superheated steam is used as a working substance in the operation of steam engines and steam turbines.

3. Properties of steam

The following properties of steam are always needed for the calculations of its various parameters, which are required in the operation of steam engines and steam turbines.

1. *Specific volume of steam.* It is the volume occupied by the steam per unit mass at a given temperature and pressure. It is expressed in m^3/kg and is the reciprocal of the density of steam. The specific volume of steam increases with the increase in temperature and decreases with the increase in pressure.

2. *Specific enthalpy of steam.* It is the total heat absorbed by the steam per unit mass from the freezing point of water (0°C or 273 K) to the saturation temperature (100°C or 373 K) plus the heat absorbed during evaporation. It is expressed in kJ/kg. The specific enthalpy of steam increases with the increase in temperature and pressure.

3. *Specific entropy of steam.* It is a theoretical value of heat energy, which can not be transformed into mechanical work under the given conditions of temperature or pressure. It is also called degree of disorder of the system. The most common term used is the change of entropy, which is mathematically given as :

$$\Delta s = \frac{\Delta Q}{\Delta T} = \frac{\text{Heat supplied}}{\text{Temperature of the system}}$$

It is expressed in kJ/kg K. The specific entropy of steam decreases with an increase in temperature and pressure.

4. Steam tables

The various properties of steam (such as specific volume, specific enthalpy and specific entropy) of dry saturated steam and superheated steam vary with the variations of temperature and pressure. These values were carefully determined by observations and calculations first in F.P.S. system and were made available in a tabular form known as steam tables. Later on, these values were converted into M.K.S. units and then into S.I. units. Due to conversion and rounding off the figures, there is a slight difference in the figures quoted in different books. Even some of the authors have changed these values in different editions of the same book. However, in this steam tables the author has quoted standard figures, which are widely accepted and internationally recognised.

There are two important steam tables. One of them is based in terms of temperature and the other in terms of pressure. It is a general practice to give the following tables for some important values:

1. Saturated water and steam (temperature) table
2. Saturated water and steam (pressure) table
3. Superheated steam table
4. Supercritical steam table

5. Saturated water and steam (temperature) table

It contains values of absolute pressure (in bar), specific volume (in m^3/kg), specific enthalpy (in kJ/kg) and specific entropy (in kJ/kg K) from 0°C to 374.15°C (critical temperature). A sample of this table is given below:

Tempe-rature in °C (t)	Absolute Pressure in bar (p)	Specific volume in m^3/kg		Specific enthalpy in kJ/kg			Specific entropy in kJ/kg K		
		Water (v_f)	Steam (v_g)	Water (h_f)	Evapo-ration (h_{fg})	Steam (h_g)	Water (s_f)	Evapora-tion (s_{fg})	Steam (s_g)
0	0.006 11	0.001 000	206.16	0.0	2501.6	2501.6	0.000	9.158	9.158
5	0.008 72	0.001 000	147.16	21.0	2489.7	2510.7	0.076	8.951	9.027
10	0.012 27	0.001 000	106.43	42.0	2477.9	2519.9	0.151	8.751	8.902

The use of this table is given in the following example.

Example 1. Calculate the specific enthalpy and specific entropy of 1 kg of steam at 10°C when its dryness fraction is 0.8.

Solution. Given: Mass of steam $(m) = 1$ kg; Temperature of steam $(t) = 10°C$ and dryness fraction of steam $(x) = 0.8$.

From steam tables, corresponding to a temperature of 10°C, we find that $h_f = 42.0$ kJ/kg; $h_{fg} = 2477.9$ kJ/kg; $s_f = 0.151$ kJ/kg K and $s_{fg} = 8.751$ kJ/kg K.

Specific enthalpy of the steam

We know that specific enthalpy of the steam,

$$h = m\,[h_f + x\,h_{fg}] = 1 \times [42.0 + (0.8 \times 2477.9)] = 2024.32 \text{ kJ } \textbf{Ans.}$$

Specific entropy of the steam

We also know that specific entropy of the steam,

$$s = m\,[s_f + x\,s_{fg}] = 1 \times [0.151 + (0.8 \times 8.751)] = 7.1518 \text{ kJ/kg K } \textbf{Ans.}$$

6. Staturated water and steam (pressure) tables

It contains the values of temperature (in °C), specific volume (in m^3/kg), specific enthalpy (in kJ/kg) and specific entropy (in kJ / kg K) from 0.0061 bar to 221.2 bar (critical pressure). A sample of this table is given below:

Absolute Pressure in bar (p)	Tempe-rature in °C (t)	Specific volume in m^3/kg		Specific enthalpy in kJ/kg			Specific entropy in kJ/kg K		
		Water (v_f)	Steam (v_g)	Water (h_f)	Evapo-ration (h_{fg})	Steam (h_g)	Water (s_f)	Evapora-tion (s_{fg})	Steam (s_g)
0.010	6.98	0.001 000	129.21	29.3	2485.0	2514.4	0.106	8.871	8.977
0.020	17.51	0.001 001	67.012	73.5	2460.2	2533.6	0.261	8.464	8.725
0.030	24.10	0.001 003	45.670	101.0	2444.6	2545.6	0.354	8.224	8.578

The use of this table is given in the following example.

Example 2. What is the specific enthalpy and specific entropy of 1.5 kg of steam at a pressure of 0.030 bar, when its dryness fraction is 0.6?

Solution. Given: Mass of steam $(m) = 1.5$ kg; Pressure of steam = 0.030 bar and dryness fraction of steam $(x) = 0.6$.

From steam tables, corresponding to a pressure of 0.030 bar, we find that $h_f = 101$ kJ/kg; $h_{fg} = 2444.6$ kJ/kg; $s_f = 0.354$ kJ/kg K and $s_{fg} = 8.224$ kJ/kg K.

Specific enthalpy of the steam

We know that specific enthalpy of the steam,

$$h = m\,[h_f + x\,h_{fg}] = 1 \times [101 + (0.6 \times 2444.6)] = 1567.76 \text{ kJ } \textbf{Ans.}$$

Specific entropy of the steam

We also know that specific entropy of the steam,

$$s = m\,[s_f + x\,s_{fg}] = 1.5 \times [0.354 + (0.6 \times 8.224)] = 7.9326 \text{ kJ/kg K } \textbf{Ans.}$$

7. Superheated steam tables

These tables contain the values of specific volume, specific enthalpy and specific entropy of superheated steam from an absolute pressure of 0.02 bar to 221.2 bar (critical pressure) at various temperatures from 100°C to 800°C. In these tables, the values of specific volume, specific enthalpy and specific entropy of steam are directly read from the concerned tables. However, the value at any other pressure or temperature, not mentioned in the tables, is obtained by interpolation.

8. Supercritical steam tables

These tables also contain the values of specific volume, specific enthalpy and specific entropy of supercritical steam from an absolute pressure of 250 bar to 1000 bar at various temperatures from 400°C to 800°C. In these tables also, the values of specific volume, specific enthalpy and specific entropy of steam are directly read from the concerned tables. However, the value at any other pressure or temperature, not mentioned in the table, is obtained by interpolation.

9. Mollier diagram

It is a graphical representation of steam tables, in which specific entropy is plotted along the ordinate (X-axis) and specific enthalpy along the abscissa (Y-axis). The diagram is divided into two portions by a somewhat horizontal line termed as saturation curve. The lower portion (*i.e.*, wet steam region) contains the values of wet steam, whereas the upper portion (*i.e.*, superheated steam region) contains the values of superheated steam. A Mollier diagram has the following lines.

    1. Dryness fraction lines

    2. Constant specific volume lines

    3. Constant pressure lines

    4. Constant temperature lines

10. Dryness fraction lines

These lines are drawn in the wet steam region. *i.e.*, only below the saturation curve (which represents dryness fraction equal to unity). These lines represent the condition of wet steam between various values of enthalpy and entropy. The dryness fraction lines are slightly curved in horizontal direction.

11. Constant specific volume lines

These lines are drawn in both the wet steam region and superheated steam region. These lines represent the specific volume of steam between the various values of enthalpy and entropy. The lines are straight in the wet steam region, *i.e.*, below the saturation curve, but are curved upwards in the superheated region *i.e.*, above the saturation curve.

12. Constant pressure lines

These lines are also drawn in both the wet steam region and superheated steam region. These lines represent the pressure of steam between the various values of enthalpy and entropy. The pressure lines are also straight in the wet steam region, *i.e.*, below the saturation curve, but are curved slightly upwards in the superheated region *i.e.*, above the saturation curve.

13. Constant temperature lines

These lines are drawn only in the superheated steam region *i.e.*, above the saturation curve. These lines represent the temperature of steam between the various values of enthalpy and entropy The temperature lines are slightly curved in the horizontal direction.

CONTENTS

TABLE 1

Staturated Water and Steam (Temperature) Tables

Temperature in °C (t)	Absolute pressure in bar (p)	Specific volume in m³/kg		Specific enthalpy in kJ/kg			Specific entropy in kJ/kg K			Temperature in °C (t)
		Water (v_f)	Steam (v_g)	Water (h_f)	Evaporation (h_{fg})	Steam (h_g)	Water (s_f)	Evaporation (s_{fg})	Steam (s_g)	
0	0.006 11	0.001 000	206.31	0.0	2 501.6	2 501.6	0.000	9.158	9.158	0
1	0.006 57	0.001 000	192.61	4.2	2 499.2	2 503.4	0.015	9.116	9.131	1
2	0.007 06	0.001 000	179.92	8.4	2 496.8	2 505.2	0.031	9.074	9.105	2
3	0.007 58	0.001 000	168.17	12.6	2 494.5	2 507.1	0.046	9.033	9.079	3
4	0.008 13	0.001 000	157.27	16.8	2 492.1	2 508.9	0.061	8.992	9.053	4
5	0.008 72	0.001 000	147.16	21.0	2 489.7	2 510.7	0.076	8.951	9.027	5
6	0.009 35	0.001 000	137.78	25.2	2 487.4	2 512.6	0.091	8.911	9.002	6
7	0.010 01	0.001 000	129.06	29.4	2 485.0	2 514.4	0.106	8.870	8.976	7
8	0.010 72	0.001 000	120.97	33.6	2 482.6	2 516.2	0.121	8.830	8.951	8
9	0.011 47	0.001 000	113.44	37.8	2 480.3	2 518.1	0.136	8.791	8.927	9
10	0.012 27	0.001 000	106.43	42.0	2 477.9	2 519.9	0.151	8.751	8.902	10
11	0.013 12	0.001 000	99.909	46.2	2 475.5	2 521.7	0.166	8.712	8.878	11
12	0.014 01	0.001 000	93.835	50.4	2 473.2	2 523.6	0.181	8.673	8.854	12
13	0.014 97	0.001 001	88.176	54.6	2 470.8	2 525.4	0.195	8.635	8.830	13
14	0.015 97	0.001 001	82.900	58.7	2 468.5	2 527.2	0.210	8.597	8.806	14
15	0.017 04	0.001 001	77.978	62.9	2 466.1	2 529.1	0.224	8.559	8.783	15
16	0.018 17	0.001 001	73.384	67.1	2 463.8	2 530.9	0.239	8.520	8.759	16
17	0.019 36	0.001 001	69.095	71.3	2 461.4	2 532.7	0.253	8.483	8.736	17
18	0.020 62	0.001 001	65.087	75.5	2 459.0	2 534.5	0.268	8.446	8.714	18
19	0.021 96	0.001 002	61.341	79.7	2 456.7	2 536.4	0.282	8.409	8.691	19

Saturated Water and Steam (Temperature) Tables

(t)	(p)	(v_f)	(v_g)	(h_f)	(h_fg)	(h_g)	(s_f)	(s_fg)	(s_g)	(t)
20	0.023 37	0.001 002	57.838	83.9	2 454.3	2 538.2	0.296	8.372	8.668	**20**
21	0.024 85	0.001 002	54.561	88.0	2 452.0	2 540.0	0.310	8.336	8.646	**21**
22	0.026 42	0.001 002	51.492	92.2	2 449.6	2 541.8	0.325	8.299	8.624	**22**
23	0.028 08	0.001 002	48.619	96.4	2 447.2	2 543.6	0.339	8.263	8.602	**23**
24	0.029 82	0.001 002	45.926	100.6	2 444.9	2 545.5	0.353	8.228	8.581	**24**
25	0.031 66	0.001 003	43.402	104.8	2 442.5	2 547.3	0.367	8.192	8.559	**25**
26	0.033 60	0.001 003	41.034	108.9	2 440.2	2 549.1	0.381	8.157	8.538	**26**
27	0.035 64	0.001 003	38.813	113.1	2 437.8	2 550.9	0.395	8.122	8.517	**27**
28	0.037 78	0.001 004	36.728	117.3	2 435.4	2 552.7	0.409	8.087	8.496	**28**
29	0.040 04	0.001 004	34.769	121.5	2 433.1	2 554.5	0.423	8.052	8.475	**29**
30	0.042 42	0.001 004	32.929	125.7	2 430.7	2 556.4	0.437	8.018	8.455	**30**
31	0.044 91	0.001 005	31.199	129.8	2 428.3	2 558.2	0.450	7.984	8.434	**31**
32	0.047 53	0.001 005	29.572	134.0	2 425.9	2 560.0	0.464	7.950	8.414	**32**
33	0.050 29	0.001 005	28.042	138.2	2 423.6	2 561.8	0.478	7.916	8.394	**33**
34	0.053 18	0.001 006	26.601	142.4	2 421.2	2 563.6	0.491	7.883	8.374	**34**
35	0.056 22	0.001 006	25.245	146.6	2 418.8	2 565.4	0.505	7.849	8.354	**35**
36	0.059 40	0.001 006	23.967	150.7	2 416.4	2 567.2	0.518	7.817	8.335	**36**
37	0.062 74	0.001 007	22.763	154.9	2 414.1	2 569.0	0.532	7.783	8.315	**37**
38	0.066 24	0.001 007	21.627	159.1	2 411.7	2 570.8	0.545	7.751	8.296	**38**
39	0.069 91	0.001 007	20.557	163.3	2 409.3	2 572.6	0.559	7.718	8.277	**39**
40	0.073 75	0.001 008	19.546	167.5	2 406.9	2 574.4	0.572	7.686	8.258	**40**
41	0.077 77	0.001 008	18.592	171.6	2 404.5	2 576.2	0.585	7.654	8.239	**41**
42	0.081 99	0.001 009	17.692	175.8	2 402.1	2 577.9	0.599	7.622	8.221	**42**
43	0.086 39	0.001 009	16.841	180.0	2 399.7	2 579.7	0.612	7.591	8.203	**43**
44	0.091 00	0.001 009	16.036	184.2	2 397.3	2 581.5	0.625	7.559	8.184	**44**
45	0.095 82	0.001 010	15.276	188.4	2 394.9	2 583.3	0.638	7.528	8.166	**45**
46	0.100 80	0.001 010	14.557	192.5	2 392.5	2 585.1	0.651	7.497	8.148	**46**
47	0.106 12	0.001 011	13.877	196.7	2 390.1	2 586.9	0.664	7.466	8.130	**47**
48	0.111 62	0.001 011	13.233	200.9	2 387.7	2 588.6	0.678	7.435	8.113	**48**
49	0.117 36	0.001 012	12.623	205.1	2 385.3	2 590.4	0.691	7.404	8.095	**49**

Saturated Water and Steam (Temperature) Tables

(t)	(p)	(v_f)	(v_g)	(h_f)	(h_fg)	(h_g)	(s_f)	(s_fg)	(s_g)	(t)
50	0.123 35	0.001 012	12.046	209.3	2 382.9	2 592.2	0.704	7.374	8.078	50
51	0.129 61	0.001 013	11.499	213.4	2 380.5	2 593.9	0.716	7.344	8.060	51
52	0.136 11	0.001 013	10.980	217.6	2 378.1	2 595.7	0.729	7.314	8.043	52
53	0.142 93	0.001 014	10.488	221.8	2 375.7	2 597.5	0.742	7.284	8.026	53
54	0.150 02	0.001 014	10.022	226.0	2 373.2	2 599.2	0.755	7.254	8.009	54
55	0.157 41	0.001 015	9.578 9	230.2	2 370.8	2 601.0	0.768	7.225	7.993	55
56	0.165 11	0.001 015	9.158 7	234.3	2 368.4	2 602.7	0.780	7.196	7.976	56
57	0.173 13	0.001 016	8.759 8	238.5	2 366.0	2 604.5	0.793	7.166	7.959	57
58	0.181 47	0.001 016	8.380 8	242.7	2 363.5	2 606.2	0.806	7.137	7.943	58
59	0.190 16	0.001 017	8.020 8	246.9	2 361.1	2 608.0	0.818	7.109	7.927	59
60	0.199 20	0.001 017	7.678 5	251.1	2 358.6	2 609.7	0.831	7.080	7.911	60
61	0.208 61	0.001 018	7.353 2	255.3	2 356.1	2 611.4	0.844	7.051	7.895	61
62	0.218 38	0.001 018	7.043 7	259.5	2 353.7	2 613.2	0.856	7.023	7.879	62
63	0.228 55	0.001 019	6.749 3	263.6	2 351.3	2 614.9	0.868	6.995	7.863	63
64	0.239 12	0.001 019	6.469 0	267.8	2 348.8	2 616.6	0.881	6.967	7.848	64
65	0.250 09	0.001 020	6.202 3	272.0	2 346.4	2 618.4	0.893	6.939	7.832	65
66	0.261 50	0.001 020	5.948 2	276.2	2 343.9	2 620.1	0.906	6.911	7.817	66
67	0.273 34	0.001 021	5.706 2	280.4	2 341.4	2 621.8	0.918	6.884	7.802	67
68	0.285 63	0.001 022	5.475 6	284.6	2 338.9	2 623.5	0.930	6.856	7.786	68
69	0.298 38	0.001 022	5.255 8	288.8	2 336.4	2 625.2	0.943	6.828	7.771	69
70	0.311 62	0.001 023	5.046 3	293.0	2 333.9	2 626.9	0.955	6.802	7.757	70
71	0.325 35	0.001 024	4.846 4	297.2	2 331.4	2 628.6	0.967	6.775	7.742	71
72	0.339 58	0.001 024	4.655 7	301.3	2 329.0	2 630.3	0.979	6.748	7.727	72
73	0.354 34	0.001 025	4.473 7	305.5	2 326.5	2 632.0	0.991	6.721	7.712	73
74	0.369 64	0.001 025	4.300 0	309.7	2 324.0	2 633.7	1.003	6.695	7.698	74
75	0.385 49	0.001 026	4.134 1	313.9	2 321.5	2 635.4	1.015	6.668	7.683	75
76	0.401 91	0.001 027	3.975 7	318.1	2 318.9	2 637.0	1.027	6.642	7.669	76
77	0.418 91	0.001 027	3.824 3	322.3	2 316.4	2 638.7	1.039	6.616	7.655	77
78	0.436 52	0.001 028	3.679 6	326.5	2 313.9	2 640.4	1.051	6.590	7.641	78
79	0.454 74	0.001 029	3.541 3	330.7	2 311.4	2 642.1	1.063	6.564	7.627	79

4

Saturated Water and Steam (Temperature) Tables

(t)	(p)	(v_f)	(v_g)	(h_f)	(h_fg)	(h_g)	(s_f)	(s_fg)	(s_g)	(t)
80	0.473 60	0.001 029	3.409 1	334.9	2 308.9	2 643.8	1.075	6.538	7.613	80
81	0.493 11	0.001 030	3.282 6	339.1	2 306.3	2 645.4	1.087	6.512	7.599	81
82	0.513 29	0.001 031	3.161 6	343.3	2 303.8	2 647.1	1.099	6.487	7.586	82
83	0.534 16	0.001 031	3.045 8	347.5	2 301.2	2 648.7	1.111	6.461	7.572	83
84	0.555 73	0.001 032	2.935 0	351.7	2 298.7	2 650.4	1.123	6.436	7.559	84
85	0.578 03	0.001 033	2.828 8	355.9	2 296.1	2 652.0	1.134	6.411	7.545	85
86	0.601 08	0.001 033	2.727 2	360.1	2 293.5	2 653.6	1.146	6.386	7.532	86
87	0.624 89	0.001 034	2.629 8	364.3	2 291.0	2 655.3	1.158	6.361	7.519	87
88	0.649 48	0.001 035	2.536 5	368.5	2 288.4	2 656.9	1.169	6.337	7.506	88
89	0.674 87	0.001 035	2.447 0	372.7	2 285.8	2 658.5	1.181	6.312	7.493	89
90	0.701 09	0.001 036	2.361 3	376.9	2 283.2	2 660.1	1.193	6.287	7.480	90
91	0.728 15	0.001 037	2.279 1	381.1	2 280.6	2 661.7	1.204	6.263	7.467	91
92	0.756 06	0.001 038	2.200 2	385.4	2 278.0	2 663.4	1.216	6.238	7.454	92
93	0.784 89	0.001 038	2.124 5	389.6	2 275.4	2 665.0	1.227	6.215	7.442	93
94	0.814 61	0.001 039	2.051 9	393.8	2 272.8	2 666.6	1.239	6.190	7.429	94
95	0.845 26	0.001 040	1.982 2	398.0	2 270.1	2 668.1	1.250	6.167	7.417	95
96	0.876 86	0.001 041	1.915 3	402.2	2 267.5	2 669.7	1.261	6.143	7.404	96
97	0.909 44	0.001 041	1.851 0	406.4	2 264.9	2 671.3	1.273	6.119	7.392	97
98	0.943 01	0.001 042	1.789 3	410.6	2 262.3	2 672.9	1.284	6.096	7.380	98
99	0.977 61	0.001 043	1.730 0	414.8	2 259.6	2 674.4	1.296	6.072	7.368	99
100	1.013 3	0.001 044	1.673 0	419.1	2 256.9	2 676.0	1.307	6.048	7.355	100
102	1.087 6	0.001 045	1.565 5	427.5	2 251.6	2 679.1	1.329	6.002	7.331	102
104	1.166 8	0.001 047	1.466 2	435.9	2 246.3	2 682.2	1.352	5.956	7.308	104
106	1.250 4	0.001 048	1.374 2	444.4	2 240.9	2 685.3	1.374	5.910	7.284	106
108	1.339 0	0.001 050	1.288 9	452.9	2 235.4	2 688.3	1.396	5.865	7.261	108
110	1.432 7	0.001 052	1.209 9	461.3	2 230.0	2 691.3	1.418	5.821	7.239	110
112	1.531 6	0.001 054	1.136 6	469.8	2 224.5	2 694.3	1.440	5.776	7.216	112
114	1.636 2	0.001 055	1.068 5	478.3	2 218.9	2 697.2	1.462	5.732	7.194	114
116	1.746 5	0.001 057	1.005 2	486.7	2 213.5	2 700.2	1.484	5.688	7.172	116
118	1.862 8	0.001 059	0.946 34	495.2	2 207.9	2 703.1	1.506	5.645	7.151	118

Saturated Water and Steam (Temperature) Tables

(t)	(s_g)	(s_{fg})	(s_f)	(h_g)	(h_{fg})	(h_f)	(v_g)	(v_f)	(p)	(t)
120	7.129	5.601	1.528	2 706.0	2 202.3	503.7	0.891 52	0.001 061	1.985 4	120
122	7.108	5.559	1.549	2 708.8	2 196.6	512.2	0.840 45	0.001 063	2.114 5	122
124	7.087	5.517	1.570	2 711.6	2 190.9	520.7	0.792 83	0.001 064	2.250 4	124
126	7.067	5.475	1.592	2 714.4	2 185.2	529.2	0.748 40	0.001 066	2.393 3	126
128	7.046	5.433	1.613	2 717.2	2 179.4	537.8	0.706 91	0.001 068	2.543 5	128
130	7.026	5.392	1.634	2 719.9	2 173.6	546.3	0.668 14	0.001 070	2.701 3	130
132	7.006	5.351	1.655	2 722.6	2 167.8	554.8	0.631 88	0.001 072	2.867 0	132
134	6.986	5.310	1.676	2 725.3	2 161.9	563.4	0.597 95	0.001 074	3.040 7	134
136	6.967	5.270	1.697	2 727.9	2 155.9	572.0	0.566 18	0.001 076	3.222 9	136
138	6.947	5.229	1.718	2 730.5	2 150.0	580.5	0.536 41	0.001 078	3.413 8	138
140	6.928	5.189	1.739	2 733.1	2 144.0	589.1	0.508 49	0.001 080	3.613 9	140
142	6.910	5.150	1.760	2 735.6	2 137.9	597.7	0.482 30	0.001 082	3.823 1	142
144	6.891	5.111	1.780	2 738.1	2 131.8	606.3	0.457 71	0.001 084	4.042 0	144
146	6.872	5.071	1.801	2 740.6	2 125.7	614.9	0.434 60	0.001 086	4.270 9	146
148	6.854	5.033	1.821	2 743.0	2 119.5	623.5	0.412 88	0.001 089	4.510 1	148
150	6.836	4.994	1.842	2 745.4	2 113.2	632.2	0.392 45	0.001 091	4.760 0	150
155	6.791	4.899	1.892	2 751.2	2 097.4	653.8	0.346 44	0.001 096	5.433 3	155
160	6.748	4.805	1.943	2 756.7	2 081.2	675.5	0.306 76	0.001 102	6.180 6	160
165	6.705	4.713	1.992	2 762.0	2 064.8	697.2	0.272 40	0.001 108	7.007 7	165
170	6.663	4.621	2.042	2 767.1	2 048.0	719.1	0.242 55	0.001 114	7.920 2	170
175	6.622	4.531	2.091	2 771.8	2 030.7	741.1	0.216 54	0.001 121	8.924 4	175
180	6.582	4.443	2.139	2 776.3	2 013.2	763.1	0.193 80	0.001 128	10.027	180
185	6.542	4.355	2.187	2 780.4	1 995.1	785.3	0.173 86	0.001 135	11.233	185
190	6.504	4.268	2.236	2 784.3	1 976.8	807.5	0.156 32	0.001 142	12.551	190
195	6.465	4.182	2.283	2 787.8	1 957.9	829.9	0.140 84	0.001 149	13.987	195
200	6.428	4.097	2.331	2 790.9	1 938.5	852.4	0.127 16	0.001 156	15.549	200
205	6.391	4.013	2.378	2 793.8	1 918.8	875.0	0.115 03	0.001 164	17.243	205
210	6.354	3.929	2.425	2 796.2	1 898.5	897.7	0.104 24	0.001 172	19.077	210
215	6.317	3.846	2.471	2 798.3	1 877.7	920.6	0.094 625	0.001 181	21.060	215
220	6.282	3.764	2.518	2 799.9	1 856.2	943.7	0.086 038	0.001 190	23.198	220

Saturated Water and Steam (Temperature) Tables

(t)	(p)	(v_f)	(v_g)	(h_f)	(h_fg)	(h_g)	(s_f)	(s_fg)	(s_g)	(t)
225	25.501	0.001 199	0.078 349	966.9	1 834.3	2 801.2	2.564	3.682	6.246	225
230	27.976	0.001 209	0.071 450	990.3	1 811.7	2 802.0	2.610	3.601	6.211	230
235	30.632	0.001 219	0.065 245	1 013.8	1 788.5	2 802.3	2.656	3.519	6.175	235
240	33.478	0.001 229	0.059 654	1 037.6	1 764.6	2 802.2	2.702	3.439	6.141	240
245	36.523	0.001 240	0.054 606	1 061.6	1 740.0	2 801.6	2.748	3.358	6.106	245
250	39.776	0.001 251	0.050 037	1 085.8	1 714.6	2 800.4	2.794	3.277	6.071	250
255	43.246	0.001 263	0.045 896	1 110.2	1 688.5	2 798.7	2.839	3.197	6.036	255
260	46.943	0.001 276	0.042 134	1 134.9	1 661.5	2 796.4	2.885	3.116	6.001	260
265	50.877	0.001 289	0.038 710	1 159.9	1 633.6	2 793.5	2.931	3.035	5.966	265
270	55.058	0.001 303	0.035 588	1 185.2	1 604.7	2 789.9	2.976	2.954	5.930	270
275	59.496	0.001 317	0.032 736	1 210.8	1 574.7	2 785.5	3.022	2.873	5.895	275
280	64.202	0.001 332	0.030 126	1 236.8	1 543.6	2 780.4	3.068	2.790	5.858	280
285	69.186	0.001 349	0.027 733	1 263.2	1 511.3	2 774.5	3.115	2.707	5.822	285
290	74.461	0.001 366	0.025 535	1 290.0	1 477.6	2 767.6	3.161	2.624	5.785	290
295	80.037	0.001 384	0.023 513	1 317.3	1 442.5	2 759.8	3.208	2.539	5.747	295
300	85.927	0.001 404	0.021 649	1 345.0	1 406.0	2 751.0	3.255	2.453	5.708	300
305	92.144	0.001 425	0.019 927	1 373.4	1 367.7	2 741.1	3.303	2.366	5.669	305
310	98.700	0.001 448	0.018 334	1 402.4	1 327.6	2 730.0	3.351	2.277	5.628	310
315	105.61	0.001 473	0.016 856	1 432.1	1 285.5	2 717.6	3.400	2.186	5.586	315
320	112.89	0.001 500	0.015 480	1 462.6	1 241.1	2 703.7	3.450	2.092	5.542	320
325	120.56	0.001 529	0.014 195	1 494.0	1 194.0	2 688.0	3.501	1.996	5.497	325
330	128.63	0.001 562	0.012 989	1 526.5	1 143.7	2 670.2	3.553	1.896	5.449	330
335	137.12	0.001 598	0.011 854	1 560.2	1 089.5	2 649.7	3.606	1.792	5.398	335
340	146.05	0.001 639	0.010 780	1 595.5	1 030.7	2 626.2	3.662	1.681	5.343	340
345	155.45	0.001 686	0.009 7631	1 632.5	966.4	2 598.9	3.719	1.564	5.283	345
350	165.35	0.001 741	0.008 7991	1 671.9	895.8	2 567.7	3.780	1.438	5.218	350
355	175.77	0.001 809	0.007 8592	1 716.6	813.8	2 530.4	3.849	1.295	5.144	355
360	186.75	0.001 896	0.006 9398	1 764.2	721.2	2 485.4	3.921	1.139	5.060	360
365	198.33	0.002 016	0.006 0116	1 818.0	610.0	2 428.0	4.002	0.956	4.958	365
370	210.54	0.002 214	0.004 9728	1 890.2	452.6	2 342.8	4.111	0.703	4.814	370
374.15	221.20	0.003 170	0.003 170	2 107.4	0.0	2 107.4	4.443	0.000	4.443	374.15

TABLE 2

Staturated Water and Steam (Pressure) Tables

Absolute pressure in bar (p)	Temperature in °C (t)	Specific volume in m³/kg		Specific enthalpy in kJ/kg			Specific entropy in kJ/kg K			Absolute pressure in bar (p)
		water (v_f)	Steam (v_g)	Water (h_f)	Evaporation (h_{fg})	Steam (h_g)	Water (s_f)	Evaporation (s_{fg})	Steam (s_g)	
0.006 1	0.000	0.001 000	206.31	0.0	2 501.6	2 501.6	0.000	9.158	9.158	**0.006 1**
0.010	6.983	0.001 000	129.21	29.3	2 485.1	2 514.4	0.106	8.871	8.977	**0.010**
0.015	13.04	0.001 001	87.982	54.7	2 470.8	2 525.5	0.196	8.634	8.830	**0.015**
0.020	17.51	0.001 001	67.006	73.5	2 460.1	2 533.6	0.261	8.464	8.725	**0.020**
0.025	21.10	0.001 002	54.256	88.4	2 451.8	2 540.2	0.312	8.333	8.645	**0.025**
0.030	24.10	0.001 003	45.667	101.0	2 444.6	2 545.6	0.354	8.224	8.578	**0.030**
0.035	26.69	0.001 003	39.479	111.8	2 438.6	2 550.4	0.391	8.132	8.523	**0.035**
0.040	28.98	0.001 004	34.802	121.4	2 433.1	2 554.5	0.423	8.053	8.476	**0.040**
0.045	31.03	0.001 005	31.141	130.0	2 428.2	2 558.2	0.451	7.983	8.434	**0.045**
0.050	32.90	0.001 005	28.194	137.8	2 423.8	2 561.6	0.476	7.920	8.396	**0.050**
0.06	36.18	0.001 006	23.741	151.5	2 416.0	2 567.5	0.521	7.810	8.331	**0.06**
0.07	39.03	0.001 007	20.531	163.4	2 409.2	2 572.6	0.559	7.718	8.277	**0.07**
0.08	41.53	0.001 008	18.105	173.9	2 403.2	2 577.1	0.593	7.637	8.230	**0.08**
0.09	43.79	0.001 009	16.204	183.3	2 397.8	2 581.1	0.622	7.566	8.188	**0.09**
0.10	45.83	0.001 010	14.675	191.8	2 392.9	2 584.7	0.649	7.502	8.151	**0.10**
0.11	47.71	0.001 011	13.416	199.7	2 388.4	2 588.1	0.674	7.444	8.118	**0.11**
0.12	49.45	0.001 012	12.362	206.9	2 384.3	2 591.2	0.696	7.391	8.087	**0.12**
0.13	51.06	0.001 013	11.466	213.7	2 380.3	2 594.0	0.717	7.342	8.059	**0.13**
0.14	52.57	0.001 013	10.694	220.0	2 376.7	2 596.7	0.737	7.296	8.033	**0.14**
0.15	54.00	0.001 014	10.023	226.0	2 373.2	2 599.2	0.755	7.254	8.009	**0.15**

Saturated Water and Steam (Pressure) Tables

(p)	(t)	(v_f)	(v_g)	(h_f)	(h_{fg})	(h_g)	(s_f)	(s_{fg})	(s_g)	(p)
0.16	55.34	0.001 015	9.433 1	231.6	2 370.0	2 601.6	0.772	7.215	7.987	0.16
0.17	56.62	0.001 015	8.911 1	236.9	2 366.9	2 603.8	0.788	7.178	7.966	0.17
0.18	57.83	0.001 016	8.445 2	242.0	2 363.9	2 605.9	0.804	7.142	7.946	0.18
0.19	58.98	0.001 017	8.027 2	246.8	2 361.1	2 607.9	0.818	7.109	7.927	0.19
0.20	60.09	0.001 017	7.649 8	251.5	2 358.4	2 609.9	0.832	7.077	7.909	0.20
0.21	61.15	0.001 018	7.307 3	255.9	2 355.8	2 611.7	0.845	7.047	7.892	0.21
0.22	62.16	0.001 018	6.995 1	260.1	2 353.4	2 613.5	0.858	7.018	7.876	0.22
0.23	63.14	0.001 019	6.709 3	264.2	2 351.0	2 615.2	0.870	6.991	7.861	0.23
0.24	64.08	0.001 019	6.446 7	268.2	2 348.6	2 616.8	0.882	6.964	7.846	0.24
0.25	64.99	0.001 020	6.204 5	272.0	2 346.3	2 618.3	0.893	6.939	7.832	0.25
0.26	65.87	0.001 020	5.980 3	275.7	2 344.2	2 619.9	0.904	6.915	7.819	0.26
0.27	66.72	0.001 021	5.772 4	279.2	2 342.1	2 621.3	0.915	6.891	7.806	0.27
0.28	67.55	0.001 021	5.577 8	282.7	2 340.0	2 622.7	0.925	6.868	7.793	0.28
0.29	68.35	0.001 022	5.398 2	286.0	2 338.1	2 624.1	0.935	6.847	7.781	0.29
0.30	69.12	0.001 022	5.229 3	289.3	2 336.1	2 625.4	0.944	6.825	7.769	0.30
0.32	70.62	0.001 023	4.922 0	295.6	2 332.4	2 628.0	0.962	6.785	7.747	0.32
0.34	72.03	0.001 024	4.650 4	301.5	2 328.9	2 630.4	0.980	6.747	7.727	0.34
0.36	73.37	0.001 025	4.407 6	307.1	2 325.5	2 632.6	0.996	6.711	7.707	0.36
0.38	74.66	0.001 026	4.190 0	312.5	2 322.3	2 634.8	1.011	6.677	7.688	0.38
0.40	75.89	0.001 027	3.993 4	317.7	2 319.2	2 636.9	1.026	6.645	7.671	0.40
0.42	77.06	0.001 027	3.814 8	322.6	2 316.3	2 638.9	1.040	6.614	7.654	0.42
0.44	78.19	0.001 028	3.652 2	327.3	2 313.4	2 640.7	1.054	6.584	7.638	0.44
0.46	79.28	0.001 029	3.503 2	331.9	2 310.7	2 642.6	1.067	6.556	7.623	0.46
0.48	80.33	0.001 029	3.366 3	336.3	2 308.0	2 644.3	1.079	6.530	7.609	0.48
0.50	81.35	0.001 030	3.240 1	340.6	2 305.4	2 646.0	1.091	6.504	7.595	0.50
0.52	82.33	0.001 031	3.123 3	344.7	2 302.9	2 647.6	1.103	6.478	7.581	0.52
0.54	83.28	0.001 031	3.014 8	348.7	2 300.5	2 649.2	1.114	6.455	7.569	0.54
0.56	84.19	0.001 032	2.913 9	352.5	2 298.2	2 650.7	1.125	6.431	7.556	0.56
0.58	85.09	0.001 033	2.819 7	356.3	2 295.8	2 652.1	1.135	6.409	7.544	0.58
0.60	85.95	0.001 033	2.731 7	359.9	2 293.7	2 653.6	1.145	6.388	7.533	0.60

Saturated Water and Steam (Pressure) Tables

9

(p)	(t)	(v_f)	(v_g)	(h_f)	(h_{fg})	(h_g)	(s_f)	(s_{fg})	(s_g)	(p)
0.62	86.80	0.001 034	2.649 1	363.5	2 291.4	2 654.9	1.155	6.367	7.522	0.62
0.64	87.62	0.001 034	2.571 5	366.9	2 289.4	2 656.3	1.165	6.346	7.511	0.64
0.66	88.42	0.001 035	2.498 5	370.3	2 287.3	2 657.6	1.174	6.326	7.500	0.66
0.68	89.20	0.001 036	2.429 7	373.6	2 285.2	2 658.8	1.183	6.307	7.490	0.68
0.70	89.96	0.001 036	2.364 7	376.8	2 283.3	2 660.1	1.192	6.288	7.480	0.70
0.72	90.70	0.001 037	2.303 1	379.9	2 281.4	2 661.3	1.201	6.270	7.471	0.72
0.74	91.43	0.001 037	2.244 8	382.9	2 279.5	2 662.4	1.209	6.253	7.462	0.74
0.76	92.14	0.001 038	2.189 5	385.9	2 277.7	2 663.6	1.217	6.235	7.452	0.76
0.78	92.83	0.001 038	2.136 9	388.9	2 275.8	2 664.7	1.225	6.219	7.444	0.78
0.80	93.51	0.001 039	2.086 9	391.7	2 274.1	2 665.8	1.233	6.202	7.435	0.80
0.85	95.15	0.001 040	1.972 1	398.6	2 269.8	2 668.4	1.252	6.163	7.415	0.85
0.90	96.71	0.001 041	1.869 1	405.2	2 265.7	2 670.9	1.270	6.125	7.395	0.90
0.95	98.20	0.001 042	1.777 1	411.5	2 261.7	2 673.2	1.287	6.091	7.378	0.95
1.00	99.63	0.001 043	1.693 8	417.5	2 257.9	2 675.4	1.303	6.057	7.360	1.00
1.013 25	100.00	0.001 044	1.673 0	419.1	2 256.9	2 676.0	1.307	6.048	7.355	1.013 25
1.05	101.0	0.001 045	1.618 1	423.3	2 254.3	2 677.6	1.318	6.025	7.343	1.05
1.10	102.3	0.001 046	1.549 2	428.8	2 250.8	2 679.6	1.333	5.995	7.328	1.10
1.15	103.6	0.001 047	1.486 1	434.2	2 247.4	2 681.6	1.347	5.966	7.313	1.15
1.20	104.8	0.001 048	1.428 1	439.3	2 244.1	2 683.4	1.361	5.937	7.298	1.20
1.25	106.0	0.001 049	1.374 6	444.4	2 240.8	2 685.2	1.374	5.911	7.285	1.25
1.30	107.1	0.001 050	1.325 0	449.2	2 237.8	2 687.0	1.387	5.885	7.272	1.30
1.35	108.2	0.001 050	1.279 1	453.4	2 234.8	2 688.7	1.399	5.860	7.259	1.35
1.40	109.3	0.001 051	1.236 3	458.4	2 231.9	2 690.3	1.411	5.836	7.247	1.40
1.45	110.4	0.001 052	1.196 3	462.8	2 229.0	2 691.8	1.423	5.812	7.235	1.45
1.50	111.4	0.001 053	1.159 0	467.1	2 226.3	2 693.4	1.433	5.790	7.223	1.50
1.60	113.3	0.001 055	1.091 1	475.4	2 220.8	2 696.2	1.455	5.747	7.202	1.60
1.70	115.2	0.001 056	1.030 9	483.2	2 215.8	2 699.0	1.475	5.706	7.181	1.70
1.80	116.9	0.001 058	0.977 18	490.7	2 210.8	2 701.5	1.494	5.668	7.162	1.80
1.90	118.6	0.001 059	0.928 95	497.9	2 206.1	2 704.0	1.513	5.631	7.144	1.90
2.00	120.2	0.001 061	0.885 40	504.7	2 201.6	2 706.3	1.530	5.597	7.127	2.00

Saturated Water and Steam (Pressure) Tables

(p)	(t)	(v_f)	(v_g)	(h_f)	(h_{fg})	(h_g)	(s_f)	(s_{fg})	(s_g)	(t)
2.1	121.8	0.001 062	0.845 86	511.3	2 197.2	2 708.5	1.547	5.564	7.111	2.1
2.2	123.3	0.001 064	0.809 80	517.6	2 193.0	2 710.6	1.563	5.532	7.095	2.2
2.3	124.7	0.001 065	0.776 77	523.7	2 188.9	2 712.6	1.578	5.502	7.080	2.3
2.4	126.1	0.001 066	0.746 41	529.6	2 184.9	2 714.5	1.593	5.473	7.066	2.4
2.5	127.4	0.001 068	0.718 40	535.3	2 181.1	2 716.4	1.607	5.445	7.052	2.5
2.6	128.7	0.001 069	0.692 47	540.9	2 177.3	2 718.2	1.621	5.418	7.039	2.6
2.7	130.0	0.001 070	0.668 40	546.2	2 173.7	2 719.9	1.634	5.392	7.026	2.7
2.8	131.2	0.001 071	0.646 00	551.4	2 170.1	2 721.5	1.647	5.367	7.014	2.8
2.9	132.4	0.001 072	0.625 09	556.5	2 166.6	2 723.1	1.660	5.342	7.002	2.9
3.0	133.5	0.001 074	0.605 53	561.5	2 163.2	2 724.7	1.672	5.319	6.991	3.0
3.1	134.7	0.001 075	0.587 18	566.2	2 159.9	2 726.1	1.683	5.297	6.980	3.1
3.2	135.8	0.001 076	0.569 95	570.9	2 156.7	2 727.6	1.695	5.274	6.969	3.2
3.3	136.8	0.001 077	0.553 73	575.5	2 153.5	2 729.0	1.706	5.253	6.959	3.3
3.4	137.9	0.001 078	0.538 43	579.9	2 150.4	2 730.3	1.717	5.232	6.949	3.4
3.5	138.9	0.001 079	0.523 97	584.3	2 147.3	2 731.6	1.727	5.212	6.939	3.5
3.6	139.9	0.001 080	0.510 29	588.5	2 144.4	2 732.9	1.738	5.192	6.930	3.6
3.7	140.8	0.001 081	0.497 33	592.7	2 141.4	2 734.1	1.748	5.173	6.921	3.7
3.8	141.8	0.001 082	0.485 02	596.7	2 138.6	2 735.3	1.758	5.154	6.912	3.8
3.9	142.7	0.001 083	0.473 33	600.8	2 135.7	2 736.5	1.767	5.136	6.903	3.9
4.0	143.6	0.001 084	0.462 20	604.7	2 132.9	2 737.6	1.776	5.118	6.894	4.0
4.1	144.5	0.001 085	0.451 59	608.5	2 130.2	2 738.7	1.786	5.100	6.886	4.1
4.2	145.4	0.001 086	0.441 47	612.3	2 127.5	2 739.8	1.795	5.083	6.878	4.2
4.3	146.3	0.001 087	0.431 81	616.0	2 124.9	2 740.9	1.803	5.067	6.870	4.3
4.4	147.1	0.001 088	0.422 57	619.6	2 122.3	2 741.9	1.812	5.050	6.862	4.4
4.5	147.9	0.001 089	0.413 73	623.2	2 119.7	2 742.9	1.820	5.035	6.855	4.5
4.6	148.7	0.001 090	0.405 26	626.7	2 117.2	2 743.9	1.829	5.018	6.847	4.6
4.7	149.5	0.001 090	0.397 14	630.1	2 114.7	2 744.8	1.837	5.003	6.840	4.7
4.8	150.3	0.001 091	0.389 34	633.5	2 112.2	2 745.7	1.845	4.988	6.833	4.8
4.9	151.1	0.001 092	0.381 86	636.8	2 109.8	2 746.6	1.853	4.973	6.826	4.9
5.0	151.8	0.001 093	0.374 66	640.1	2 107.4	2 747.5	1.860	4.959	6.819	5.0

Saturated Water and Steam (Pressure) Tables

(p)	(t)	(v_f)	(v_g)	(h_f)	(h_{fg})	(h_g)	(s_f)	(s_{fg})	(s_g)	(p)
5.2	153.3	0.001 095	0.361 06	646.5	2 102.7	2 749.2	1.875	4.931	6.806	5.2
5.4	154.8	0.001 096	0.348 44	652.8	2 098.1	2 750.9	1.890	4.903	6.793	5.4
5.6	156.2	0.001 098	0.336 69	658.8	2 093.7	2 752.5	1.904	4.877	6.781	5.6
5.8	157.5	0.001 099	0.325 72	664.7	2 089.3	2 754.0	1.918	4.851	6.769	5.8
6.0	158.8	0.001 101	0.315 46	670.4	2 085.1	2 755.5	1.931	4.827	6.758	6.0
6.2	160.1	0.001 102	0.305 84	676.1	2 080.8	2 756.9	1.944	4.803	6.747	6.2
6.4	161.4	0.001 104	0.296 80	681.5	2 076.7	2 758.2	1.956	4.780	6.736	6.4
6.6	162.6	0.001 105	0.288 29	686.8	2 072.7	2 759.5	1.968	4.757	6.725	6.6
6.8	163.8	0.001 107	0.280 26	692.0	2 068.8	2 760.8	1.980	4.735	6.715	6.8
7.0	165.0	0.001 108	0.272 68	697.1	2 064.9	2 762.0	1.992	4.713	6.705	7.0
7.2	166.1	0.001 110	0.265 50	702.0	2 061.2	2 763.2	2.003	4.693	6.696	7.2
7.4	167.2	0.001 111	0.258 70	706.9	2 057.4	2 764.3	2.014	4.672	6.686	7.4
7.6	168.3	0.001 112	0.252 24	711.7	2 053.7	2 765.4	2.025	4.652	6.677	7.6
7.8	169.4	0.001 114	0.246 10	716.3	2 050.1	2 766.4	2.035	4.633	6.668	7.8
8.0	170.4	0.001 115	0.240 26	720.9	2 046.5	2 767.4	2.046	4.614	6.660	8.0
8.2	171.4	0.001 116	0.234 69	725.4	2 043.0	2 768.4	2.056	4.595	6.651	8.2
8.4	172.4	0.001 118	0.229 38	729.9	2 039.6	2 769.4	2.066	4.577	6.643	8.4
8.6	173.4	0.001 119	0.224 31	734.2	2 036.2	2 770.4	2.075	4.560	6.635	8.6
8.8	174.4	0.001 120	0.219 46	738.5	2 032.8	2 771.3	2.085	4.542	6.627	8.8
9.0	175.4	0.001 121	0.214 82	742.6	2 029.5	2 772.1	2.094	4.525	6.619	9.0
9.2	176.3	0.001 123	0.210 37	746.8	2 026.2	2 773.0	2.103	4.509	6.612	9.2
9.4	177.2	0.001 124	0.206 10	750.8	2 023.0	2 773.8	2.112	4.492	6.604	9.4
9.6	178.1	0.001 125	0.202 01	754.8	2 019.8	2 774.6	2.121	4.476	6.597	9.6
9.8	179.0	0.001 126	0.198 08	758.7	2 016.7	2 775.4	2.130	4.460	6.590	9.8
10.0	179.9	0.001 127	0.194 30	762.6	2 013.6	2 776.2	2.138	4.445	6.583	10.0
10.5	182.0	0.001 130	0.185 48	772.0	2 006.0	2 778.0	2.159	4.407	6.566	10.5
11.0	184.1	0.001 133	0.177 39	781.1	1 998.6	2 779.7	2.179	4.371	6.550	11.0
11.5	186.0	0.001 136	0.170 02	789.9	1 991.4	2 781.3	2.198	4.336	6.534	11.5
12.0	188.0	0.001 139	0.163 21	798.4	1 984.3	2 782.7	2.216	4.303	6.519	12.0
12.5	189.8	0.001 141	0.156 96	806.7	1 977.5	2 784.2	2.234	4.271	6.505	12.5

Saturated Water and Steam (Pressure) Tables

(p)	(t)	(v_f)	(v_g)	(h_f)	(h_fg)	(h_g)	(s_f)	(s_fg)	(s_g)	(p)
13.0	191.6	0.001 144	0.151 14	814.7	1 970.7	2 785.4	2.251	4.240	6.491	13.0
13.5	193.3	0.001 146	0.145 76	822.5	1 964.2	2 786.7	2.267	4.211	6.478	13.5
14.0	195.0	0.001 149	0.140 73	830.1	1 957.7	2 787.8	2.284	4.181	6.465	14.0
14.5	196.7	0.001 151	0.136 06	837.5	1 951.4	2 788.9	2.299	4.154	6.453	14.5
15.0	198.3	0.001 154	0.131 67	844.6	1 945.3	2 789.9	2.314	4.127	6.441	15.0
15.5	199.8	0.001 156	0.127 56	851.6	1 939.2	2 790.8	2.329	4.100	6.429	15.5
16.0	201.4	0.001 159	0.123 70	858.5	1 933.2	2 791.7	2.344	4.074	6.418	16.0
16.5	202.9	0.001 161	0.120 06	865.3	1 927.3	2 792.6	2.358	4.049	6.407	16.5
17.0	204.3	0.001 163	0.116 64	871.8	1 921.6	2 793.4	2.371	4.025	6.396	17.0
17.5	205.7	0.001 166	0.113 40	878.2	1 915.9	2 794.1	2.384	4.001	6.385	17.5
18.0	207.1	0.001 168	0.110 33	884.5	1 910.3	2 794.8	2.398	3.977	6.375	18.0
18.5	208.5	0.001 170	0.107 42	890.7	1 904.8	2 795.5	2.410	3.955	6.365	18.5
19.0	209.8	0.001 172	0.104 67	896.8	1 899.3	2 796.1	2.423	3.933	6.356	19.0
19.5	211.1	0.001 174	0.102 04	902.7	1 894.0	2 796.7	2.435	3.911	6.346	19.5
20.0	212.4	0.001 177	0.099 55	908.5	1 888.7	2 797.2	2.447	3.890	6.337	20.0
21.0	214.8	0.001 181	0.094 902	919.9	1 878.3	2 798.2	2.470	3.849	6.319	21.0
22.0	217.2	0.001 185	0.090 663	930.9	1 868.1	2 799.1	2.492	3.809	6.301	22.0
23.0	219.6	0.001 189	0.086 780	941.6	1 858.2	2 799.8	2.514	3.771	6.285	23.0
24.0	221.8	0.001 193	0.083 209	951.9	1 848.5	2 800.4	2.534	3.735	6.269	24.0
25.0	223.9	0.001 197	0.079 915	961.9	1 839.1	2 801.0	2.554	3.699	6.253	25.0
26.0	226.0	0.001 201	0.076 865	971.7	1 829.7	2 801.4	2.574	3.665	6.239	26.0
27.0	228.1	0.001 205	0.074 033	981.2	1 820.5	2 801.7	2.592	3.632	6.224	27.0
28.0	230.0	0.001 209	0.071 396	990.5	1 811.5	2 802.0	2.611	3.600	6.211	28.0
29.0	232.0	0.001 213	0.068 935	999.5	1 802.7	2 802.2	2.628	3.569	6.197	29.0
30.0	233.8	0.001 216	0.066 632	1 008.3	1 794.0	2 802.3	2.646	3.538	6.184	30.0
31.0	235.7	0.001 220	0.064 473	1 017.1	1 785.4	2 802.3	2.662	3.509	6.171	31.0
32.0	237.4	0.001 224	0.062 443	1 025.4	1 776.9	2 802.3	2.679	3.480	6.159	32.0
33.0	239.2	0.001 227	0.060 533	1 033.7	1 768.6	2 802.3	2.694	3.452	6.146	33.0
34.0	240.9	0.001 231	0.058 731	1 041.8	1 760.3	2 802.1	2.710	3.424	6.134	34.0
35.0	242.5	0.001 235	0.057 028	1 049.7	1 752.3	2 802.0	2.725	3.398	6.123	35.0

Saturated Water and Steam (Pressure) Tables

(p)	(t)	(v_f)	(v_g)	(h_f)	(h_{fg})	(h_g)	(s_f)	(s_{fg})	(s_g)	(p)
36.0	244.2	0.001 238	0.055 417	1 057.5	1 744.2	2 801.7	2.740	3.371	6.111	36.0
37.0	245.8	0.001 242	0.053 889	1 065.2	1 736.2	2 801.4	2.755	3.345	6.100	37.0
38.0	247.3	0.001 245	0.052 439	1 072.7	1 728.4	2 801.1	2.769	3.321	6.090	38.0
39.0	248.8	0.001 249	0.051 061	1 080.1	1 720.7	2 800.8	2.783	3.296	6.079	39.0
40.0	250.3	0.001 252	0.049 749	1 087.4	1 712.9	2 800.3	2.797	3.272	6.069	40.0
42.0	253.2	0.001 259	0.047 306	1 101.6	1 697.8	2 799.4	2.823	3.225	6.048	42.0
44.0	256.1	0.001 266	0.045 078	1 115.4	1 682.9	2 798.3	2.849	3.180	6.029	44.0
46.0	258.8	0.001 273	0.043 036	1 128.8	1 668.2	2 797.0	2.874	3.136	6.010	46.0
48.0	261.4	0.001 279	0.041 158	1 141.8	1 653.9	2 795.7	2.897	3.094	5.991	48.0
50.0	263.9	0.001 286	0.039 425	1 154.5	1 639.7	2 794.2	2.921	3.053	5.974	50.0
52.0	266.4	0.001 293	0.037 820	1 166.9	1 625.7	2 792.6	2.943	3.013	5.956	52.0
54.0	268.8	0.001 299	0.036 330	1 179.0	1 611.8	2 790.8	2.965	2.974	5.939	54.0
56.0	271.1	0.001 306	0.034 942	1 190.8	1 598.2	2 789.0	2.986	2.937	5.923	56.0
58.0	273.4	0.001 312	0.033 646	1 202.4	1 584.6	2 787.0	3.007	2.899	5.906	58.0
60.0	275.6	0.001 319	0.032 433	1 213.7	1 571.3	2 785.0	3.027	2.863	5.890	60.0
62.0	277.7	0.001 325	0.031 295	1 224.9	1 558.0	2 782.9	3.047	2.828	5.875	62.0
64.0	279.8	0.001 332	0.030 225	1 235.8	1 544.8	2 780.6	3.066	2.794	5.860	64.0
66.0	281.9	0.001 338	0.029 218	1 246.5	1 531.8	2 778.3	3.085	2.760	5.845	66.0
68.0	283.9	0.001 345	0.028 267	1 257.1	1 518.8	2 775.9	3.104	2.727	5.831	68.0
70.0	285.8	0.001 351	0.027 368	1 267.4	1 506.0	2 773.4	3.122	2.694	5.816	70.0
72.0	287.7	0.001 358	0.026 517	1 277.7	1 493.2	2 770.9	3.140	2.662	5.802	72.0
74.0	289.6	0.001 365	0.025 711	1 287.8	1 480.4	2 768.2	3.157	2.631	5.788	74.0
76.0	291.4	0.001 371	0.024 944	1 297.7	1 467.8	2 765.5	3.174	2.600	5.774	76.0
78.0	293.2	0.001 378	0.024 215	1 307.5	1 455.4	2 762.7	3.191	2.569	5.760	78.0
80.0	295.0	0.001 384	0.023 521	1 317.2	1 442.7	2 759.9	3.208	2.539	5.747	80.0
82.0	296.7	0.001 391	0.022 860	1 326.7	1 430.3	2 757.0	3.224	2.510	5.734	82.0
84.0	298.4	0.001 398	0.022 228	1 336.2	1 417.8	2 754.0	3.240	2.481	5.721	84.0
86.0	300.1	0.001 404	0.021 624	1 345.4	1 405.5	2 750.9	3.256	2.452	5.708	86.0
88.0	301.7	0.001 411	0.021 046	1 354.7	1 393.1	2 747.8	3.271	2.424	5.695	88.0
90.0	303.3	0.001 418	0.020 493	1 363.8	1 380.8	2 744.6	3.287	2.395	5.682	90.0

Saturated Water and Steam (Pressure) Tables

(p)	(t)	(v_f)	(v_g)	(h_f)	(h_{fg})	(h_g)	(s_f)	(s_{fg})	(s_g)	(p)
92	304.9	0.001 425	0.019 962	1 372.8	1 368.5	2 741.3	3.302	2.367	5.669	92
94	306.5	0.001 432	0.019 453	1 381.7	1 356.3	2 738.0	3.317	2.340	5.657	94
96	308.0	0.001 439	0.018 964	1 390.6	1 344.1	2 734.7	3.332	2.313	5.644	96
98	309.5	0.001 446	0.018 493	1 399.4	1 331.9	2 731.2	3.346	2.286	5.632	98
100	311.0	0.001 453	0.018 041	1 408.0	1 319.7	2 727.7	3.361	2.259	5.620	100
105	314.6	0.001 470	0.016 981	1 429.5	1 289.2	2 718.7	3.396	2.194	5.590	105
110	318.0	0.001 489	0.016 007	1 450.5	1 258.8	2 709.3	3.430	2.129	5.560	110
115	321.4	0.001 508	0.015 114	1 471.3	1 228.2	2 699.5	3.464	2.066	5.530	115
120	324.6	0.001 527	0.014 285	1 491.7	1 197.5	2 698.2	3.497	2.003	5.500	120
125	327.8	0.001 547	0.013 518	1 511.9	1 166.5	2 678.4	3.530	1.941	5.471	125
130	330.8	0.001 567	0.012 800	1 531.9	1 135.1	2 667.0	3.561	1.880	5.441	130
135	333.8	0.001 588	0.012 130	1 551.8	1 103.3	2 655.1	3.593	1.818	5.411	135
140	336.6	0.001 611	0.011 498	1 571.5	1 070.9	2 642.4	3.624	1.756	5.380	140
145	339.4	0.001 634	0.010 905	1 591.3	1 037.9	2 629.2	3.655	1.694	5.349	145
150	342.1	0.001 658	0.010 343	1 610.9	1 004.2	2 615.1	3.686	1.632	5.318	150
155	344.8	0.001 683	0.009 813	1 630.7	969.7	2 600.4	3.716	1.570	5.286	155
160	347.3	0.001 710	0.009 310	1 650.4	934.5	2 584.9	3.747	1.506	5.253	160
165	349.7	0.001 739	0.008 833	1 670.4	898.5	2 568.9	3.778	1.442	5.220	165
170	352.3	0.001 770	0.008 372	1 691.6	860.0	2 551.6	3.811	1.375	5.186	170
175	354.6	0.001 803	0.007 927	1 713.3	820.0	2 533.3	3.844	1.306	5.150	175
180	357.0	0.001 840	0.007 497	1 734.8	779.1	2 513.9	3.877	1.236	5.113	180
185	359.2	0.001 881	0.007 082	1 756.5	736.5	2 493.0	3.910	1.164	5.074	185
190	361.4	0.001 926	0.006 676	1 778.7	691.8	2 470.5	3.943	1.090	5.033	190
195	363.6	0.001 978	0.006 276	1 801.9	643.9	2 445.8	3.978	1.011	4.989	195
200	365.7	0.002 037	0.005 875	1 826.6	591.6	2 418.2	4.015	0.926	4.941	200
205	367.8	0.002 110	0.005 462	1 854.2	532.0	2 386.2	4.056	0.830	4.886	205
210	369.8	0.002 202	0.005 023	1 886.3	461.2	2 347.5	4.105	0.717	4.822	210
215	371.8	0.002 342	0.004 509	1 929.4	365.2	2 294.6	4.170	0.566	4.736	215
220	373.7	0.002 668	0.003 735	2 010.3	186.3	2 196.6	4.293	0.288	4.581	220
221.2	374.15	0.003 170	0.003 170	2 107.4	000.0	2 107.4	4.443	0.000	4.443	221.2

TABLE 3

Specific Volume of Superheated Steam

Absolute Pressure in bar (p)	Saturation Temperature in °C (t_s)	Specific volume (v) in m³/kg at various temperatures in °C										
		100	150	200	250	300	350	400	500	600	700	800
0.02	17.5	86.08	97.63	109.2	120.7	132.2	143.8	155.3	178.4	201.5	224.6	247.6
0.04	29.0	43.03	48.81	54.58	60.35	66.12	71.89	77.66	89.20	100.7	112.3	123.8
0.06	36.2	28.68	32.53	36.38	40.23	44.08	47.93	51.77	59.47	67.16	74.85	82.54
0.08	41.5	21.50	24.40	27.28	30.17	33.06	35.94	38.83	44.60	50.37	56.14	61.91
0.10	45.8	17.20	19.51	21.83	24.14	26.45	28.75	31.06	35.68	40.30	44.91	49.53
0.15	54.0	11.51	13.06	14.61	16.16	17.71	19.25	20.80	23.89	26.98	30.07	33.16
0.20	60.1	8.585	9.748	10.91	12.07	13.22	14.37	15.53	17.84	20.15	22.45	24.76
0.25	65.0	6.874	7.808	8.737	9.665	10.59	11.52	12.44	14.29	16.14	17.99	19.84
0.30	69.1	5.714	6.493	7.268	8.040	8.811	9.581	10.35	11.89	13.43	14.70	16.51
0.35	72.7	4.898	5.568	6.233	6.896	7.557	8.218	8.879	10.20	11.52	12.84	14.16
0.40	75.9	4.279	4.866	5.448	6.028	6.607	7.185	7.763	8.918	10.07	11.23	12.38
0.45	78.7	3.803	4.325	4.844	5.360	5.875	6.389	6.903	7.930	8.957	9.984	10.99
0.50	81.3	3.418	3.889	4.356	4.821	5.284	5.747	6.209	7.134	8.057	8.981	9.904
0.60	86.0	2.844	3.238	3.628	4.016	4.402	4.788	5.174	5.944	6.714	7.484	8.254
0.70	90.0	2.434	2.773	3.108	3.441	3.772	4.103	4.434	5.095	5.755	6.415	7.074
0.80	93.5	2.126	2.425	2.718	3.010	3.300	3.590	3.879	4.457	5.035	5.613	6.190
0.90	96.7	1.887	2.153	2.415	2.674	2.933	3.190	3.448	3.962	4.475	4.989	5.502
1.00	99.6	1.696	1.936	2.172	2.406	2.639	2.871	3.103	3.565	4.028	4.490	4.952
1.50	111.4	...	1.285	1.444	1.601	1.757	1.912	2.067	2.376	2.685	2.993	3.301
2.00	120.2	...	0.959 5	1.080	1.199	1.316	1.433	1.549	1.781	2.013	2.244	2.475

Specific Volume of Superheated Steam

(p)	(ts)	100	150	200	250	300	350	400	500	600	700	800
2.5	127.4	..	0.764 1	0.862 0	0.957 4	1.052	1.145	1.239	1.424	1.610	1.795	1.980
3.0	133.5	..	0.633 7	0.716 4	0.796 4	0.875 3	0.953 5	1.031	1.187	1.341	1.496	1.650
3.5	138.9	..	0.540 6	0.612 3	0.681 4	0.749 3	0.816 6	0.883 5	1.017	1.149	1.282	1.414
4.0	143.6	..	0.470 7	0.534 3	0.595 2	0.654 9	0.713 9	0.772 5	0.889 2	1.005	1.121	1.237
4.5	147.9	..	0.416 5	0.473 8	0.528 4	0.581 7	0.634 3	0.686 5	0.790 5	0.893 9	0.997 1	1.100
5.0	151.8	..	..	0.425 0	0.474 4	0.522 6	0.570 1	0.617 2	0.710 8	0.804 0	0.896 9	0.989 6
6.0	158.8	..	..	0.352 0	0.393 9	0.434 4	0.474 2	0.513 6	0.591 8	0.669 6	0.747 1	0.824 5
7.0	165.0	..	..	0.299 9	0.336 4	0.371 4	0.405 7	0.439 6	0.506 9	0.573 7	0.640 2	0.706 6
8.0	170.4	..	..	0.260 8	0.293 2	0.324 1	0.354 3	0.384 2	0.443 2	0.501 7	0.560 0	0.618 1
9.0	175.4	..	..	0.230 3	0.259 6	0.287 4	0.314 4	0.341 0	0.393 6	0.445 8	0.497 6	0.549 3
10.0	179.9	..	..	0.205 9	0.232 8	0.258 0	0.282 4	0.306 5	0.354 0	0.401 0	0.447 7	0.494 3
11.0	184.1	..	..	0.185 9	0.210 8	0.233 9	0.256 3	0.278 2	0.321 5	0.364 4	0.406 9	0.449 2
12.0	188.0	..	..	0.169 2	0.192 4	0.213 9	0.234 5	0.254 7	0.294 5	0.333 8	0.372 9	0.411 8
13.0	191.6	..	..	0.155 1	0.176 9	0.196 9	0.216 1	0.234 8	0.271 6	0.308 0	0.344 1	0.380 0
14.0	195.0	..	..	0.142 9	0.163 6	0.182 3	0.200 2	0.217 7	0.252 0	0.285 9	0.319 4	0.352 8
15.0	198.3	..	..	0.132 4	0.152 0	0.169 7	0.186 5	0.202 9	0.235 0	0.266 7	0.298 0	0.329 2
16.0	201.4	..	..	...	0.141 9	0.158 7	0.174 5	0.190 0	0.220 2	0.249 9	0.279 3	0.308 6
17.0	204.3	..	..	...	0.132 9	0.148 9	0.164 0	0.178 6	0.207 0	0.235 1	0.262 8	0.290 4
18.0	207.1	..	..	...	0.125 0	0.140 2	0.154 6	0.168 4	0.195 4	0.221 9	0.248 1	0.274 2
19.0	209.8	..	..	...	0.117 9	0.132 5	0.146 1	0.159 3	0.184 9	0.210 1	0.235 0	0.259 7
20.0	212.4	..	..	...	0.111 5	0.125 5	0.138 6	0.151 1	0.175 6	0.199 5	0.223 2	0.246 7
22.0	217.2	..	..	...	0.100 4	0.113 4	0.125 5	0.137 0	0.159 3	0.181 2	0.202 8	0.224 2
24.0	221.8	..	..	...	0.091 08	0.103 4	0.114 6	0.125 2	0.145 8	0.165 9	0.185 8	0.205 4
26.0	226.0	..	..	...	0.083 21	0.094 83	0.105 3	0.115 3	0.134 4	0.153 0	0.171 4	0.189 5
28.0	230.0	..	..	...	0.076 44	0.087 51	0.097 40	0.106 7	0.124 6	0.141 9	0.159 0	0.175 9
30.0	233.8	..	..	...	0.070 55	0.081 16	0.090 53	0.099 31	0.116 1	0.132 3	0.148 3	0.164 1
32.0	237.4	..	..	...	0.065 38	0.075 59	0.084 51	0.092 83	0.108 7	0.123 9	0.139 0	0.153 8
34.0	240.9	..	..	...	0.060 80	0.070 68	0.079 20	0.087 11	0.102 1	0.116 5	0.130 7	0.144 7
36.0	244.2	..	..	...	0.056 70	0.066 30	0.074 48	0.082 02	0.096 26	0.110 0	0.123 4	0.136 6
38.0	247.3	..	..	...	0.053 02	0.062 37	0.070 25	0.077 47	0.091 04	0.104 1	0.116 8	0.129 4

Specific Volume of Superheated Steam

(p)	(t$_s$)	100	150	200	250	300	350	400	500	600	700	800
40.0	250.3	...	...	...	...	0.058 83	0.066 45	0.073 38	0.086 34	0.098 76	0.110 9	0.122 9
42.0	253.2	...	...	...	...	0.055 63	0.063 00	0.069 67	0.082 09	0.093 97	0.105 6	0.117 0
44.0	256.0	...	...	...	...	0.052 70	0.059 86	0.066 30	0.078 23	0.089 61	0.100 7	0.111 6
46.0	258.8	...	...	...	...	0.050 03	0.056 99	0.063 22	0.074 70	0.085 62	0.096 26	0.106 7
48.0	261.4	...	...	...	...	0.047 57	0.054 36	0.060 39	0.071 47	0.081 97	0.092 19	0.102 2
50.0	263.9	...	...	...	...	0.045 30	0.051 94	0.057 79	0.068 49	0.078 62	0.088 45	0.098 09
55.0	269.9	...	...	...	...	0.043 43	0.046 66	0.052 13	0.062 02	0.071 31	0.080 31	0.089 12
60.0	275.6	...	...	...	...	0.036 15	0.042 22	0.047 38	0.056 59	0.065 18	0.073 48	0.081 59
65.0	280.8	...	...	...	...	0.032 58	0.038 48	0.043 38	0.052 03	0.060 03	0.067 74	0.075 26
70.0	285.8	...	...	...	...	0.029 46	0.035 23	0.039 92	0.048 09	0.055 59	0.062 79	0.069 80
75.0	290.5	...	...	...	...	0.026 72	0.032 43	0.036 94	0.044 69	0.051 76	0.058 52	0.065 09
80.0	295.0	...	...	...	...	0.024 26	0.029 95	0.034 31	0.041 70	0.048 39	0.054 77	0.060 96
85.0	299.2	...	...	...	...	0.021 91	0.027 76	0.032 00	0.039 08	0.045 44	0.051 48	0.057 32
90.0	303.3	...	...	...	...	...	0.025 79	0.029 93	0.036 74	0.042 80	0.048 53	0.054 08
95.0	307.2	...	...	...	...	...	0.024 03	0.028 08	0.034 65	0.040 45	0.045 91	0.051 19
100.0	311.0	...	...	...	...	...	0.022 42	0.026 41	0.032 76	0.038 32	0.043 55	0.048 58
110.0	318.0	...	...	...	...	...	0.019 61	0.023 51	0.029 50	0.034 66	0.039 47	0.044 08
120.0	324.6	...	...	...	...	...	0.017 21	0.021 08	0.026 79	0.031 60	0.036 07	0.040 33
130.0	330.8	...	...	...	...	...	0.015 10	0.019 02	0.024 49	0.029 02	0.033 19	0.037 16
140.0	336.6	...	...	...	...	...	0.013 21	0.017 23	0.022 51	0.026 80	0.030 72	0.034 44
150.0	342.1	...	...	...	...	...	0.011 46	0.015 66	0.020 80	0.024 88	0.028 59	0.032 09
160.0	347.3	...	...	...	...	...	0.009 76	0.014 28	0.019 29	0.023 20	0.026 72	0.030 03
170.0	352.3	...	...	...	...	...	...	0.013 03	0.017 97	0.021 72	0.025 07	0.028 21
180.0	357.0	...	...	...	...	...	...	0.011 91	0.016 79	0.020 40	0.023 00	0.026 59
190.0	361.4	...	...	...	...	...	...	0.010 89	0.015 73	0.019 22	0.022 29	0.025 15
200.0	365.7	...	...	...	...	...	...	0.009 95	0.014 77	0.018 16	0.021 11	0.023 85
210.0	369.8	...	...	...	...	...	...	0.009 07	0.013 91	0.017 20	0.020 04	0.022 67
220.0	373.7	...	...	...	...	...	...	0.008 25	0.013 12	0.016 33	0.019 07	0.021 60
221.2	374.15	...	...	...	...	...	...	0.008 16	0.013 03	0.016 22	0.018 95	0.021 35

TABLE 4

Specific Enthalpy of Superheated Steam

Absolute Pressure in bar (p)	Saturation Temperature in °C (ts)	Specific enthalphy (h) in kJ/kg at various temperatures in °C										
		100	150	200	250	300	350	400	500	600	700	800
0.02	17.5	2 688.5	2 783.7	2 880.0	2 977.7	3 076.8	3 177.5	3 279.7	3 489.2	3 705.6	3 928.8	4 158.7
0.04	29.0	2 688.3	2 783.5	2 879.9	2 977.6	3 076.8	3 177.4	3 279.7	3 489.2	3 705.6	3 928.8	4 158.7
0.06	36.2	2 688.0	2 783.4	2 879.8	2 977.6	3 076.7	3 177.4	3 279.6	3 489.2	3 705.6	3 928.8	4 158.7
0.08	41.5	2 687.8	2 783.2	2 879.7	2 977.5	3 076.7	3 177.3	3 279.6	3 489.1	3 705.5	3 928.8	4 158.7
0.10	45.8	2 687.5	2 783.1	2 879.6	2 977.4	3 076.6	3 177.3	3 279.6	3 489.1	3 705.5	3 928.8	4 158.7
0.15	54.0	2 686.9	2 782.4	2 879.5	2 977.3	3 076.5	3 177.7	3 279.5	3 489.1	3 705.5	3 928.7	4 158.7
0.20	60.1	2 686.3	2 782.3	2 879.2	2 977.1	3 076.4	3 177.1	3 279.4	3 489.0	3 705.4	3 928.7	4 158.7
0.25	65.0	2 685.7	2 782.0	2 879.0	2 977.0	3 076.3	3 177.0	3 279.3	3 489.0	3 705.4	3 928.7	4 158.6
0.30	69.1	2 685.1	2 781.6	2 878.7	2 976.8	3 076.1	3 176.9	3 279.3	3 488.9	3 705.4	3 928.7	4 158.6
0.35	72.7	2 684.5	2 781.2	2 878.5	2 976.7	3 076.0	3 176.8	3 279.2	3 488.9	3 705.3	3 928.7	4 158.6
0.40	75.9	2 683.8	2 780.9	2 878.2	2 976.5	3 075.9	3 176.8	3 279.1	3 488.8	3 705.3	3 928.6	4 158.6
0.45	78.7	2 683.2	2 780.5	2 878.0	2 976.3	3 075.8	3 176.7	3 279.1	3 488.8	3 705.2	3 928.6	4 158.5
0.50	81.3	2 682.6	2 780.1	2 877.7	2 976.1	3 075.7	3 176.6	3 279.0	3 488.7	3 705.2	3 928.6	4 158.5
0.60	86.0	2 681.3	2 779.4	2 877.3	2 975.8	3 075.4	3 176.4	3 278.8	3 488.6	3 705.1	3 928.5	4 158.5
0.70	90.0	2 680.0	2 778.6	2 876.8	2 975.5	3 075.2	3 176.2	3 278.7	3 488.5	3 705.0	3 928.4	4 158.4
0.80	93.5	2 678.8	2 777.8	2 876.3	2 975.2	3 075.0	3 176.0	3 278.5	3 488.4	3 705.0	3 928.4	4 158.4
0.90	96.7	2 677.5	2 777.1	2 875.8	2 974.8	3 074.7	3 175.8	3 278.4	3 488.3	3 704.9	3 928.3	4 158.3
1.00	99.6	2 676.2	2 776.3	2 875.4	2 974.5	3 074.5	3 175.6	3 278.2	3 488.1	3 704.8	3 928.2	4 158.3
1.50	111.4	. .	2 772.5	2 872.9	2 972.9	3 073.3	3 174.7	3 277.5	3 487.6	3 704.4	3 927.9	4 158.0
2.00	120.2	. .	2 768.5	2 870.5	2 971.2	3 072.1	3 173.8	3 276.7	3 487.0	3 704.0	3 927.6	4 157.8

Specific Enthalpy of Superheated Steam

(p)	(t_s)	100	150	200	250	300	350	400	500	600	700	800
2.5	127.4	…	2 764.5	2 868.0	2 969.6	3 070.9	3 172.8	3 275.9	3 486.5	3 703.6	3 927.3	4 157.6
3.0	133.5	…	2 760.4	2 865.5	2 967.9	3 069.7	3 171.9	3 275.2	3 486.0	3 703.2	3 927.0	4 157.3
3.5	138.9	…	2 756.3	2 863.0	2 966.2	3 068.4	3 170.9	3 274.4	3 485.4	3 702.7	3 926.7	4 157.1
4.0	143.6	…	2 752.0	2 860.4	2 964.5	3 067.2	3 170.0	3 273.6	3 484.9	3 702.3	3 926.4	4 156.9
4.5	147.9	…	2 746.7	2 857.8	2 962.8	3 066.0	3 169.1	3 272.9	3 484.3	3 701.9	3 926.1	4 156.7
5.0	151.8	…	…	2 855.1	2 961.1	3 064.8	3 168.1	3 272.1	3 483.8	3 701.5	3 925.8	4 156.4
6.0	158.8	…	…	2 849.7	2 957.6	3 062.3	3 166.2	3 270.6	3 482.7	3 700.7	3 925.1	4 155.9
7.0	165.0	…	…	2 844.2	2 954.0	3 059.8	3 164.3	3 269.0	3 481.6	3 699.9	3 924.5	4 155.5
8.0	170.4	…	…	2 838.6	2 950.4	3 057.3	3 162.4	3 267.5	3 480.5	3 699.1	3 923.9	4 155.0
9.0	175.4	…	…	2 832.7	2 946.8	3 054.7	3 160.5	3 266.0	3 479.4	3 698.2	3 923.3	4 154.5
10.0	179.9	…	…	2 826.8	2 943.0	3 052.1	3 158.5	3 264.4	3 478.3	3 697.4	3 922.7	4 154.1
11.0	184.1	…	…	2 820.7	2 939.3	3 049.6	3 156.6	3 262.9	3 477.2	3 696.6	3 922.0	4 153.6
12.0	188.0	…	…	2 814.4	2 935.4	3 046.9	3 154.6	3 261.3	3 476.1	3 695.8	3 921.4	4 153.1
13.0	191.6	…	…	2 808.0	2 931.5	3 044.3	3 152.7	3 259.7	3 475.0	3 695.0	3 920.8	4 152.7
14.0	195.0	…	…	2 801.4	2 927.6	3 041.6	3 150.7	3 258.2	3 473.9	3 694.1	3 920.2	4 152.2
15.0	198.3	…	…	2 794.7	2 923.5	3 038.9	3 148.7	3 256.6	3 472.8	3 693.3	3 919.6	4 151.7
16.0	201.4	…	…	…	2 919.4	3 036.2	3 146.7	3 255.0	3 471.7	3 692.5	3 918.9	4 151.3
17.0	204.3	…	…	…	2 915.3	3 033.5	3 144.7	3 253.5	3 470.6	3 691.7	3 918.3	4 150.8
18.0	207.1	…	…	…	2 911.0	3 030.7	3 142.7	3 251.9	3 469.5	3 690.9	3 917.7	4 150.3
19.0	209.8	…	…	…	2 906.7	3 027.9	3 140.7	3 250.3	3 468.4	3 690.0	3 917.1	4 149.8
20.0	212.4	…	…	…	2 902.4	3 025.0	3 138.6	3 248.7	3 467.3	3 689.2	3 916.5	4 149.4
22.0	217.2	…	…	…	2 893.4	3 019.3	3 134.5	3 245.5	3 465.1	3 687.6	3 915.2	4 148.4
24.0	221.8	…	…	…	2 884.2	3 013.4	3 130.4	3 242.3	3 462.9	3 685.9	3 914.0	4 147.5
26.0	226.0	…	…	…	2 874.7	3 007.4	3 126.1	3 239.0	3 460.6	3 684.3	3 912.7	4 146.6
28.0	230.0	…	…	…	2 864.9	3 001.3	3 121.9	3 235.8	3 458.4	3 682.6	3 911.5	4 145.6
30.0	233.8	…	…	…	2 854.8	2 995.1	3 117.5	3 232.5	3 456.2	3 681.0	3 910.3	4 144.7
32.0	237.4	…	…	…	2 844.4	2 988.7	3 113.2	3 229.2	3 454.0	3 679.3	3 909.0	4 143.8
34.0	240.9	…	…	…	2 833.6	2 982.2	3 108.7	3 225.9	3 451.7	3 677.7	3 907.8	4 142.8
36.0	244.2	…	…	…	2 822.5	2 975.6	3 104.2	3 222.5	3 449.5	3 676.1	3 906.5	4 141.9
38.0	247.3	…	…	…	2 811.0	2 968.9	3 099.7	3 219.1	3 447.2	3 674.4	3 905.3	4 141.0

Specific Enthalpy of Superheated Steam

(p)	(t_s)	100	150	200	250	300	350	400	500	600	700	800
40.0	250.3	…	…	…	…	2 962.0	3 095.1	3 215.7	3 445.0	3 672.8	3 904.1	4 140.0
42.0	253.2	…	…	…	…	2 955.0	3 090.4	3 212.3	3 442.7	3 671.1	3 902.8	4 139.1
44.0	256.0	…	…	…	…	2 947.8	3 085.7	3 208.8	3 440.5	3 669.5	3 901.6	4 138.2
46.0	258.8	…	…	…	…	2 940.5	3 080.9	3 205.3	3 438.2	3 667.8	3 900.3	4 137.2
48.0	261.4	…	…	…	…	2 933.1	3 076.1	3 201.8	3 435.9	3 666.2	3 899.1	4 136.3
50.0	263.9	…	…	…	…	2 925.5	3 071.2	3 198.3	3 433.7	3 664.5	3 897.9	4 135.3
55.0	269.9	…	…	…	…	2 905.8	3 058.7	3 189.3	3 427.9	3 660.4	3 894.8	4 133.0
60.0	275.6	…	…	…	…	2 885.0	3 045.8	3 180.1	3 422.2	3 656.2	3 891.7	4 130.7
65.0	280.8	…	…	…	…	2 863.0	3 032.4	3 170.8	3 416.4	3 652.1	3 888.6	4 128.8
70.0	285.8	…	…	…	…	2 839.0	3 018.7	3 161.2	3 410.6	3 647.9	3 885.4	4 126.0
75.0	290.5	…	…	…	…	2 814.1	3 004.5	3 151.6	3 404.7	3 643.7	3 882.4	4 123.7
80.0	295.0	…	…	…	…	2 786.6	2 989.9	3 141.6	3 398.8	3 639.5	3 879.2	4 121.3
85.0	299.2	…	…	…	…	2 757.1	2 974.7	3 131.5	3 392.8	3 635.4	3 876.1	4 119.0
90.0	303.3	…	…	…	…	…	2 959.0	3 121.2	3 386.8	3 631.1	3 873.0	4 116.7
95.0	307.2	…	…	…	…	…	2 942.7	3 110.7	3 380.7	3 627.0	3 869.9	4 114.4
100.0	311.0	…	…	…	…	…	2 925.8	3 099.9	3 374.6	3 622.7	3 866.8	4 112.0
110.0	318.0	…	…	…	…	…	2 889.6	3 077.8	3 362.2	3 614.2	3 860.5	4 107.3
120.0	324.6	…	…	…	…	…	2 849.7	3 054.8	3 349.6	3 605.7	3 854.3	4 102.7
130.0	330.8	…	…	…	…	…	2 805.0	3 030.7	3 336.8	3 597.1	3 848.0	4 098.0
140.0	336.6	…	…	…	…	…	2 754.2	3 005.6	3 323.8	3 588.5	3 841.7	4 093.3
150.0	342.1	…	…	…	…	…	2 694.8	2 979.1	3 310.6	3 579.8	3 835.4	4 088.6
160.0	347.3	…	…	…	…	…	2 620.8	2 951.3	3 297.1	3 571.0	3 829.1	4 084.0
170.0	352.3	…	…	…	…	…	…	2 921.7	3 283.5	3 562.2	3 822.8	4 079.3
180.0	357.0	…	…	…	…	…	…	2 890.3	3 269.6	3 553.4	3 816.5	4 074.6
190.0	361.4	…	…	…	…	…	…	2 856.7	3 255.4	3 544.5	3 810.2	4 070.0
200.0	365.7	…	…	…	…	…	…	2 820.5	3 241.1	3 535.5	3 803.8	4 065.3
210.0	369.8	…	…	…	…	…	…	2 781.3	3 226.5	3 526.5	3 797.5	4 060.6
220.0	373.7	…	…	…	…	…	…	2 738.8	3 211.7	3 517.4	3 791.1	4 055.9
221.2	374.15	…	…	…	…	…	…	2 734.5	3 210.7	3 516.4	3 789.1	4 054.7

TABLE 5

Specific Entropy of Superheated Steam

Absolute Pressure in bar (p)	Saturation Temperature in °C (t_s)	Specific entropy (s) in kJ/kg K at various temperatures in °C										
		100	150	200	250	300	350	400	500	600	700	800
0.02	17.5	9.193	9.433	9.648	9.844	10.025	10.193	10.351	10.641	10.904	11.146	11.371
0.04	29.0	8.873	9.113	9.328	9.524	9.705	9.874	10.031	10.321	10.585	10.827	11.051
0.06	36.2	8.685	8.925	9.141	9.337	9.518	9.686	9.844	10.134	10.397	10.639	10.864
0.08	41.5	8.552	8.792	9.008	9.204	9.385	9.554	9.711	10.001	10.265	10.507	10.731
0.10	45.8	8.449	8.689	8.905	9.101	9.282	9.450	9.608	9.898	10.162	10.404	10.628
0.15	54.0	8.261	8.502	8.718	8.915	9.096	9.264	9.422	9.712	9.975	10.217	10.442
0.20	60.1	8.126	8.368	8.584	8.781	8.962	9.130	9.288	9.578	9.842	10.084	10.309
0.25	65.0	8.022	8.264	8.481	8.678	8.859	9.028	9.186	9.476	9.739	9.981	10.206
0.30	69.1	7.936	8.179	8.396	8.593	8.774	8.943	9.101	9.391	9.654	9.897	10.121
0.35	72.7	7.864	8.107	8.325	8.522	8.703	8.872	9.030	9.320	9.583	9.826	10.050
0.40	75.9	7.801	8.045	8.263	8.460	8.641	8.810	8.968	9.258	9.522	9.764	9.989
0.45	78.7	7.745	7.990	8.208	8.405	8.587	8.755	8.914	9.204	9.467	9.709	9.934
0.50	81.3	7.695	7.941	8.159	8.356	8.538	8.707	8.865	9.155	9.419	9.661	9.886
0.60	86.0	7.609	7.855	8.074	8.272	8.454	8.622	8.781	9.071	9.334	9.576	9.801
0.70	90.0	7.535	7.783	8.002	8.200	8.382	8.551	8.709	9.000	9.263	9.505	9.730
0.80	93.5	7.470	7.720	7.940	8.138	8.320	8.489	8.648	8.938	9.214	9.444	9.669
0.90	96.7	7.413	7.664	7.884	8.083	8.266	8.435	8.593	8.884	9.147	9.389	9.614
1.00	99.6	7.362	7.614	7.835	8.034	8.217	8.386	8.544	8.835	9.098	9.341	9.565
1.50	111.4	. .	7.419	7.644	7.845	8.028	8.198	8.356	8.647	8.911	9.153	9.378
2.00	120.2	. .	7.279	7.507	7.710	7.894	8.064	8.223	8.514	8.778	9.020	9.245

Specific Entropy of Superheated Steam

(p)	(t_s)	100	150	200	250	300	350	400	500	600	700	800
2.5	127.4	…	7.169	7.400	7.604	7.789	7.960	8.119	8.410	8.674	8.917	9.142
3.0	133.5	…	7.077	7.312	7.518	7.703	7.874	8.034	8.326	8.590	8.833	9.058
3.5	138.5	…	6.998	7.237	7.444	7.631	7.802	7.962	8.254	8.518	8.761	8.986
4.0	143.6	…	6.929	7.171	7.380	7.568	7.740	7.899	8.192	8.456	8.699	8.925
4.5	147.9	…	6.866	7.112	7.323	7.512	7.684	7.844	8.137	8.402	8.645	8.870
5.0	151.8	…	…	7.059	7.272	7.461	7.634	7.795	8.088	8.353	8.596	8.821
6.0	158.8	…	…	6.966	7.183	7.374	7.548	7.709	8.003	8.268	8.511	8.737
7.0	165.0	…	…	6.886	7.107	7.300	7.475	7.636	7.931	8.196	8.440	8.665
8.0	170.4	…	…	6.815	7.040	7.235	7.411	7.573	7.868	8.134	8.377	8.603
9.0	175.4	…	…	6.751	6.980	7.177	7.354	7.517	7.812	8.079	8.323	8.549
10.0	179.9	…	…	6.692	6.926	7.125	7.303	7.467	7.763	8.029	8.273	8.500
11.0	184.1	…	…	6.638	6.876	7.078	7.257	7.421	7.718	7.985	8.229	8.455
12.0	188.0	…	…	6.587	6.831	7.034	7.214	7.379	7.677	7.944	8.188	8.415
13.0	191.6	…	…	6.539	6.788	6.994	7.175	7.340	7.639	7.906	8.151	8.378
14.0	195.0	…	…	6.494	6.748	6.956	7.139	7.305	7.603	7.871	8.116	8.343
15.0	198.3	…	…	6.451	6.710	6.921	7.104	7.271	7.570	7.839	8.084	8.311
16.0	201.4	…	…		6.674	6.887	7.072	7.239	7.540	7.808	8.054	8.281
17.0	204.3	…	…		6.640	6.856	7.042	7.210	7.511	7.779	8.025	8.252
18.0	207.1	…	…		6.607	6.826	7.013	7.182	7.483	7.752	7.998	8.226
19.0	209.8	…	…		6.576	6.797	6.986	7.155	7.457	7.727	7.973	8.200
20.0	212.4	…	…		6.545	6.770	6.960	7.130	7.432	7.702	7.949	8.176
22.0	217.2	…	…		6.488	6.718	6.911	7.082	7.386	7.657	7.904	8.132
24.0	221.8	…	…		6.434	6.670	6.866	7.038	7.344	7.615	7.862	8.091
26.0	226.0	…	…		6.382	6.625	6.824	6.998	7.305	7.577	7.825	8.053
28.0	230.0	…	…		6.333	6.582	6.784	6.960	7.269	7.541	7.789	8.018
30.0	233.8	…	…		6.286	6.542	6.747	6.925	7.235	7.508	7.756	7.986
32.0	237.4	…	…		6.240	6.504	6.712	6.891	7.203	7.477	7.726	7.955
34.0	240.9	…	…		6.195	6.467	6.679	6.860	7.172	7.447	7.697	7.927
36.0	244.2	…	…		6.151	6.432	6.647	6.829	7.144	7.420	7.669	7.900
38.0	247.3	…	…		6.109	6.397	6.616	6.801	7.117	7.393	7.643	7.874

Specific Entropy of Superheated Steam

(p)	(t_s)	100	150	200	250	300	350	400	500	600	700	800
40.0	250.3	...	...	...	...	6.364	6.587	6.773	7.091	7.368	7.619	7.850
42.0	253.2	...	...	...	...	6.332	6.559	6.747	7.066	7.344	7.595	7.826
44.0	256.0	...	...	...	...	6.301	6.532	6.722	7.043	7.321	7.573	7.804
46.0	258.8	...	...	...	...	6.270	6.505	6.697	7.020	7.299	7.551	7.783
48.0	261.4	...	...	...	...	6.240	6.479	6.674	6.998	7.278	7.531	7.763
50.0	263.9	...	...	...	...	6.211	6.455	6.651	6.977	7.258	7.511	7.743
55.0	269.9	...	...	...	...	6.139	6.395	6.597	6.928	7.210	7.464	7.697
60.0	275.6	...	...	...	...	6.069	6.339	6.546	6.882	7.166	7.422	7.655
65.0	280.8	...	...	...	...	6.001	6.285	6.499	6.839	7.126	7.382	7.617
70.0	285.8	...	...	...	...	5.933	6.233	6.454	6.799	7.088	7.346	7.581
75.0	290.5	...	...	...	...	5.864	6.184	6.411	6.762	7.053	7.311	7.547
80.0	295.0	...	...	...	...	5.794	6.135	6.369	6.726	7.019	7.279	7.516
85.0	299.2	...	...	...	...	5.744	6.088	6.330	6.692	6.987	7.249	7.486
90.0	303.3	...	...	...	...	...	6.041	6.292	6.660	6.957	7.220	7.458
95.0	307.2	...	...	...	...	...	5.995	6.254	6.629	6.929	7.192	7.431
100.0	311.0	...	...	...	...	...	5.949	6.218	6.599	6.901	7.166	7.406
110.0	318.0	...	...	...	...	...	5.857	6.148	6.543	6.850	7.117	7.358
120.0	324.6	...	...	...	...	...	5.764	6.081	6.491	6.802	7.072	7.315
130.0	330.8	...	...	...	...	...	5.666	6.016	6.441	6.758	7.030	7.274
140.0	336.6	...	...	...	...	...	5.562	5.951	6.394	6.716	6.991	7.237
150.0	342.1	...	...	...	...	...	5.447	5.888	6.349	6.676	6.954	7.201
160.0	347.3	...	...	...	...	...	5.311	5.824	6.305	6.639	6.919	7.168
170.0	352.3	...	...	...	...	...	...	5.760	6.264	6.603	6.886	7.137
180.0	357.0	...	...	...	...	...	...	5.695	6.223	6.569	6.854	7.107
190.0	361.4	...	...	...	...	...	...	5.628	6.184	6.536	6.824	7.078
200.0	365.7	...	...	...	...	...	...	5.559	6.146	6.504	6.795	7.051
210.0	369.8	...	...	...	...	...	...	5.486	6.108	6.474	6.768	7.025
220.0	373.7	...	...	...	...	...	...	5.410	6.072	6.444	6.741	7.000
221.2	374.15	...	...	...	...	...	...	5.399	6.068	6.441	6.738	6.994